World Land and Water Resources

Martin Duddin

Assistant Head Teacher
Knox Academy, Haddington

Alister Hendrie

Rector
Linlathen High School, Dundee

Hodder & Stoughton

LONDON SYDNEY AUCKLAND TORONTO

Acknowledgments

The authors and publishers thank the following for permission to reproduce the photographs in this book (page numbers in the brackets): J. Allen Cash Ltd (30), Barnaby's Picture Library (21), Canada House Photo library (78, 79), Farmers' Weekly (44), Friends of the Earth (60), John and Penny Hubley (44, 45), Institute of Oceanographic Sciences (102), Middle East Archive (85), National Aeronautics and Space Administration (4), South American Pictures (65), Tennessee Valley Authority (38), USDA Soil Conservation Service (91).

The authors also wish to thank the following organisations and individuals who gave help and assistance and advice in the compilation of material for this book, particularly:

Dr Kenneth Atkinson, School of Geography, University of Leeds
Shirley Smith, British Columbia Government Office, London
Irene Cawthorn, Debbie Hewish and Ann House, Canadian High Commission, London
Earthscan, London
Information Services Branch, Ministry of Forests, Government of British Columbia, Victoria, Canada
Information Services, Government of Saskatchewan, Regina, Canada
Communications Division, Saskatchewan Wheat Pool
Ian Strong, Geography Department, Forres Academy
Lindsey Young and Duncan Lauder, Geography Department, Portobello High School, Edinburgh
Stan Cartmell and Elizabeth Scott, Geography Department, Alloa Academy
Special thanks to Mrs Irene Hendrie for collating the glossary.

British Library Cataloguing in Publication Data

Duddin, Martin K.
World land and water resources.
1. Land resources 2. Natural resources: Water
I. Title II. Hendrie, Alister J.
333.73

ISBN 0-7131-7746-2

First published 1988
Fourth impression 1991

Printed in Great Britain for the educational publishing division of Hodder and Stoughton Ltd, Mill Road, Dunton Green, Sevenoaks, Kent by St Edmundsbury Press Limited, Bury St Edmunds, Suffolk.

Contents

NB Capitalised words in the text are defined in the Glossary

1

Resources — the global concept

Introduction

From the beginning, humans have constantly assessed and reassessed what this planet of ours provides in terms of our needs; and ingenuity has gradually brought into use more and more of the naturally occurring phenomena which are found on, above or below the planet's surface. It is precisely this need and capability which bestows upon certain natural phenomena a usefulness which allows us to consider them somewhat differently, as **'resources'**. Put in simple terms, resources can be defined as 'anything provided by nature which is used by people'. This textbook seeks to examine the complex relationship which exists between the people who live on this planet and the resources it provides for our use.

One of the problems associated with resources is the fact that they are so unevenly distributed across the Earth's surface. The polar ice caps, for example, are not particularly well endowed, although their importance has increased considerably this century, whereas the temperate grasslands and forests have provided for what are now amongst some of the most economically advanced nations on Earth. Availability of perhaps the most basic resources of all, the rays of the sun and precipitation, also varies greatly, two major determining factors being latitude and distance from the sea (see chapter 2). It is equally important to realise that resource endowment in different parts of the world is something which is dynamic rather than static although processes of change have tended to be fairly slow in the past. In more recent times, however, the limited though developing ability of humans to either consciously or unconsciously alter natural conditions has resulted in more rapid change. This has given rise to some of the major environmental issues of our time, e.g. shrinking tropical rain forests, desertification and acid rain.

1.1 Satellite photograph of Earth

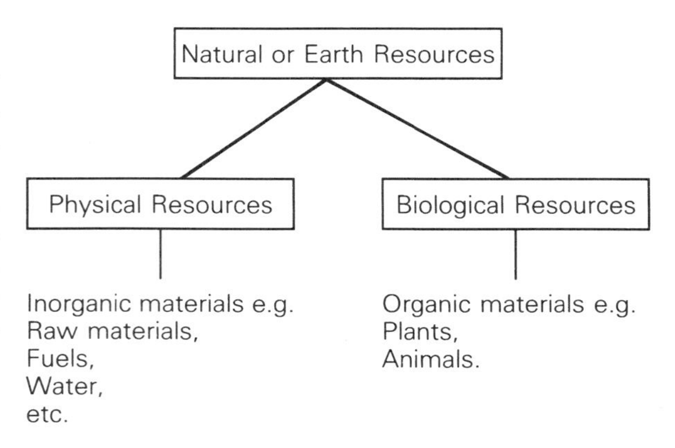

1.2 A classification of resources

Classifying resources

One possible way of classifying resources is into two broad groups: physical resources and biological resources (see Fig. 1.2). Physical resources are of an inorganic nature and consist largely of the natural materials and phenomena found above, on or near the surface of the Earth which people make direct or indirect use of in sustaining their lives. On the other hand, biological

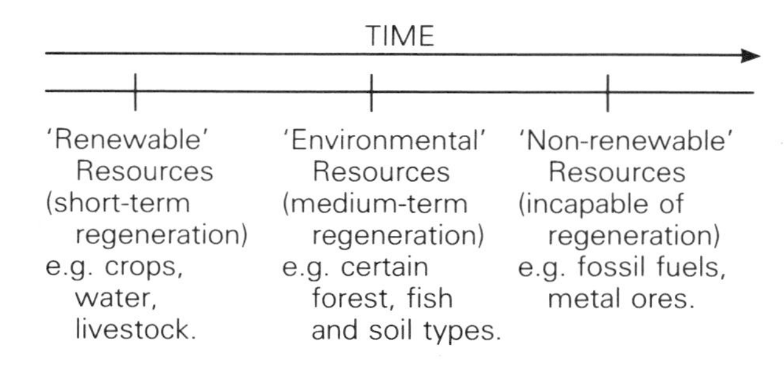

1.3 A resource 'continuum'

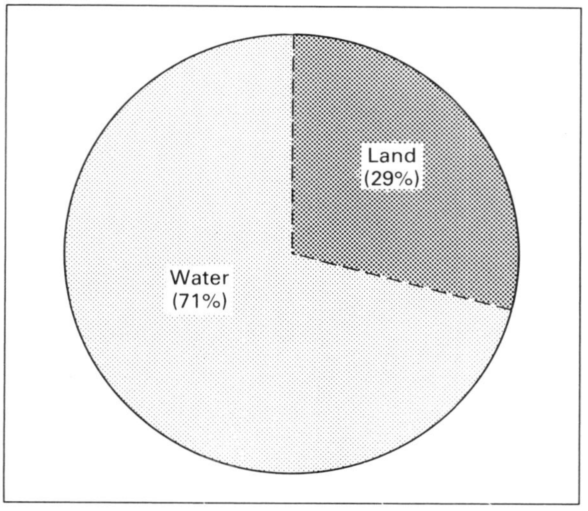

1.4 Proportion of land/water on the Earth's surface

resources are organic in nature and comprise the living plants and animals which humans make use of, and some would say exploit, for their own purposes.

As with resources in general these two types proliferate to varying degrees and form a 'resource layer' of widely differing depth across the Earth's surface.

Even more commonly, resources are classified as being renewable or non-renewable. In this case, the basic difference between them is the time span over which they develop (see Fig. 1.3). Renewable resources, e.g. crops, take a relatively short time to grow and can often be harvested several terms per year, whereas non-renewable resources, e.g. fossil fuels such as coal and oil, took millions of years to form below the surface of the Earth and once used up are lost forever. Thereafter, an alternative source of supply must normally be tapped. In some cases however, e.g. ferrous and all non-ferrous metals including those regarded as being 'precious', at least partial recycling of scrap is often possible.

As the continuum (Fig. 1.3) indicates, the time over which development takes place is the factor which divides renewable from non-renewable resources. Somewhere between the two are a group of so-called 'environmental' resources which can regenerate or recover over a medium-term time span. Resources which now fall into that category, largely as a result of human interference, include certain types of forest, some varieties of fish, and even certain soil types. Sadly, human mis-management could result in resources such as these, which previously would have been considered as being 'renewable', being lost in their entirety and incapable of regeneration.

For the purposes of this textbook, we felt obliged to classify resources by source area, starting initially with two broad categories – resources from the land and resources from water. Of the 510 million km^2 which make up the surface area of the Earth only 29% or 149 million km^2 are land, while the other 71% of 361 million km^2 are water (Fig. 1.4). The land surface of the Earth can be suitably sub-divided into a number of **'bio-climatic zones'** or **'biomes'** which vary greatly in area (Fig. 1.5) and in terms of their climatic and vegetational characteristics. Similarly, it is possible to sub-divide the Earth's water surface in a number of ways, perhaps most obviously into areas of salt water and areas of fresh water. Some 97% of the world's water resources consist of salt water, mostly found in the oceans and the seas (Fig. 1.6), and the remaining 3% consist of fresh water. Almost 75% of the fresh water, however, is frozen into the Earth's ice-caps and glaciers, leaving 24.7% as groundwater and only 0.3% in lakes and rivers.

Bioclimatic zone	**Approximate area** (millions km^2)
Tropical rain forest	17.0
Tropical grassland	15.0
Hot deserts	18.0
Monsoon lands	8.5
Mediterranean lands	7.5
Temperate grasslands and forests	21.0
Coniferous forests (taiga)	12.0
Tundra	8.0
Miscellaneous (icecap, mountains, cultivated land)	42.0
Total	149.0

1.5 Bioclimatic zones — approximate areas

Body	% (Approx.)
Oceans	97.6
Rivers (average channel storage)	0.0001
Fresh-water lakes	0.0094
Saline lakes, inland seas	0.0076
Soil moisture, vadose water*	0.0108
Ground-water	0.5060
Ice-caps, glaciers	1.925
Atmospheric vapour (water equivalent)	0.0001
Total (rounded) water in all realms	100.0

* Vadose water is water held in rocks immediately below the soil.

1.6 Water on and in the proximity of the Earth's surface

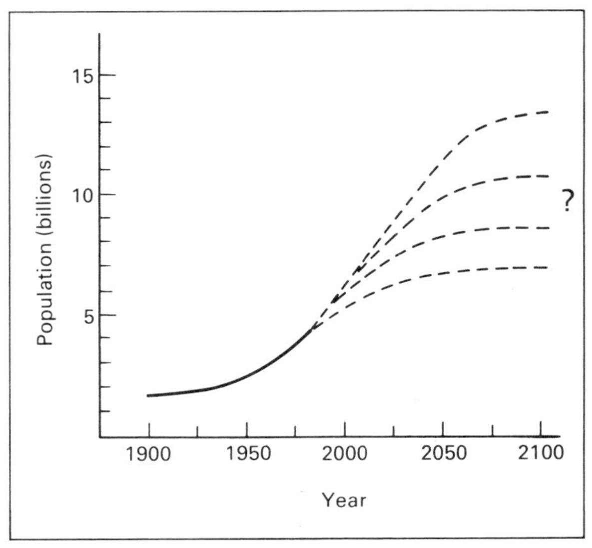

1.7 Graph of world population growth showing various projections until c. 2100

1. Draw a time-line across your page. Mark pre-historic times at one end, the present day at the other and the 'Middle Ages' somewhere in between.
   a) Below each heading, list some of the natural resources most commonly in use at each of these times.
   b) What does this suggest about the way in which human use of natural resources has changed through time?

2. With reference to the definitions of 'physical' and 'biological' resources stated at the start of the section on 'Classifying resources', put forward a case for arguing that the tropical rain forests either do or do not have a deeper 'resource layer' than the temperate grasslands and forests.

3. Study Figure 1.3.
   a) Suggest actual examples of resources which may at one time have been regarded as 'renewable' but which now would be better categorised as 'environmental'.
   b) In each case state how human interference has led to this situation.

4. Explain why the areas quoted for each bioclimatic zone in Fig. 1.5 can only be regarded as very approximate.

Increasing demands on land and water resources

The Earth's land and water resources constitute a fairly finite resource base upon which increasing world population (Fig. 1.7) has been placing greater and greater demands, especially in more recent times. These demands have been by no means uniform across the 29% of the Earth's surface which is land. This is due to the human preference to establish settlement where physical conditions have proved most favourable to the provision of that most basic of human needs, food. It has been estimated that as little as 30% of the land surface of Earth is actually suitable for cultivation, 10% of which is currently being cultivated with another 20% available to be brought into cultivation if required (Fig. 1.8). The other 70% is regarded as being unsuitable for cultivation for various different reasons. Inevitably, this contributes to a very uneven world distribution of population as shown in Fig. 1.9.

Ackerman has attempted to take all the Earth's resources, not just food, into consideration, along with population, in suggesting that the world can be divided into regions of five different 'population-resource' types. This is shown in Fig. 1.10. The

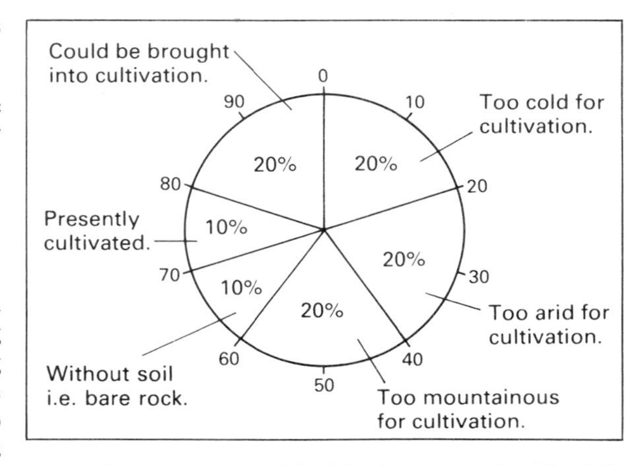

1.8 Cultivable/uncultivable land on the Earth's surface

first of these types is regarded as consisting of areas which have a highly advantageous population resource ratio where room for population expansion using technology amidst an abundant resource base still exists. In areas which are identified as being of Type 2, population and resources are regarded as being much more finely balanced and a watchful eye needs to be kept on resource use. Most regions which fall into the Type 3 category can be identified as having a plentiful resource base but a relatively low population which has not yet acquired the technological 'know-how' to make use of it to the full. The Type 4 category includes areas with existing high populations but where the resource base is limited. Type 5 consists of regions where the resource base is such that the land remains virtually uninhabited. A conceptual framework such as is provided by population-resource types should help us better understand the reasons for the very uneven distribution of world population referred to earlier and shown on Fig. 1.9.

In contrast to land resources, the salt water found in the world's oceans and many of its seas is a relatively under-used resource which has not as yet come under the same degree of pressure as certain of the Earth's land resources. Fresh water resources, which are immediately available for human use in our lakes, rivers and to some extent from below the ground, have been widely exploited, on the other hand, and problems of availability occur regularly in many parts of the world.

Today we are in a global situation where our land and water resources are in constant need of reappraisal both in terms of current levels of use of the total 'stock' and in terms of the margins most readily available for future use. It must be remembered that these margins are constantly being eaten into and are not always capable of being replenished. Constant monitoring of land and water resource use will be required in the future, especially in those regions of the world where population is unlikely to stabilise until well into the twenty-first century.

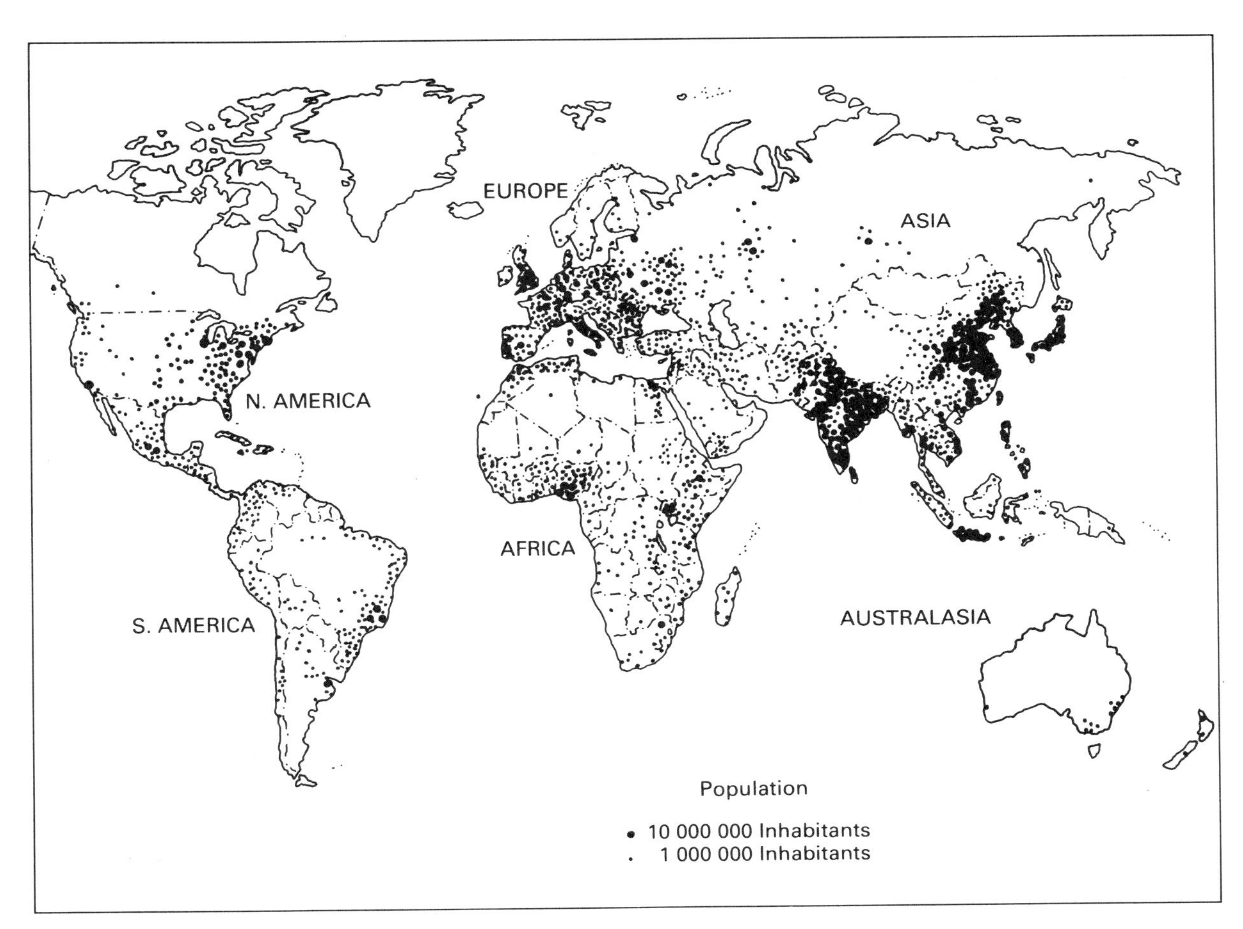

1.9 World population distribution

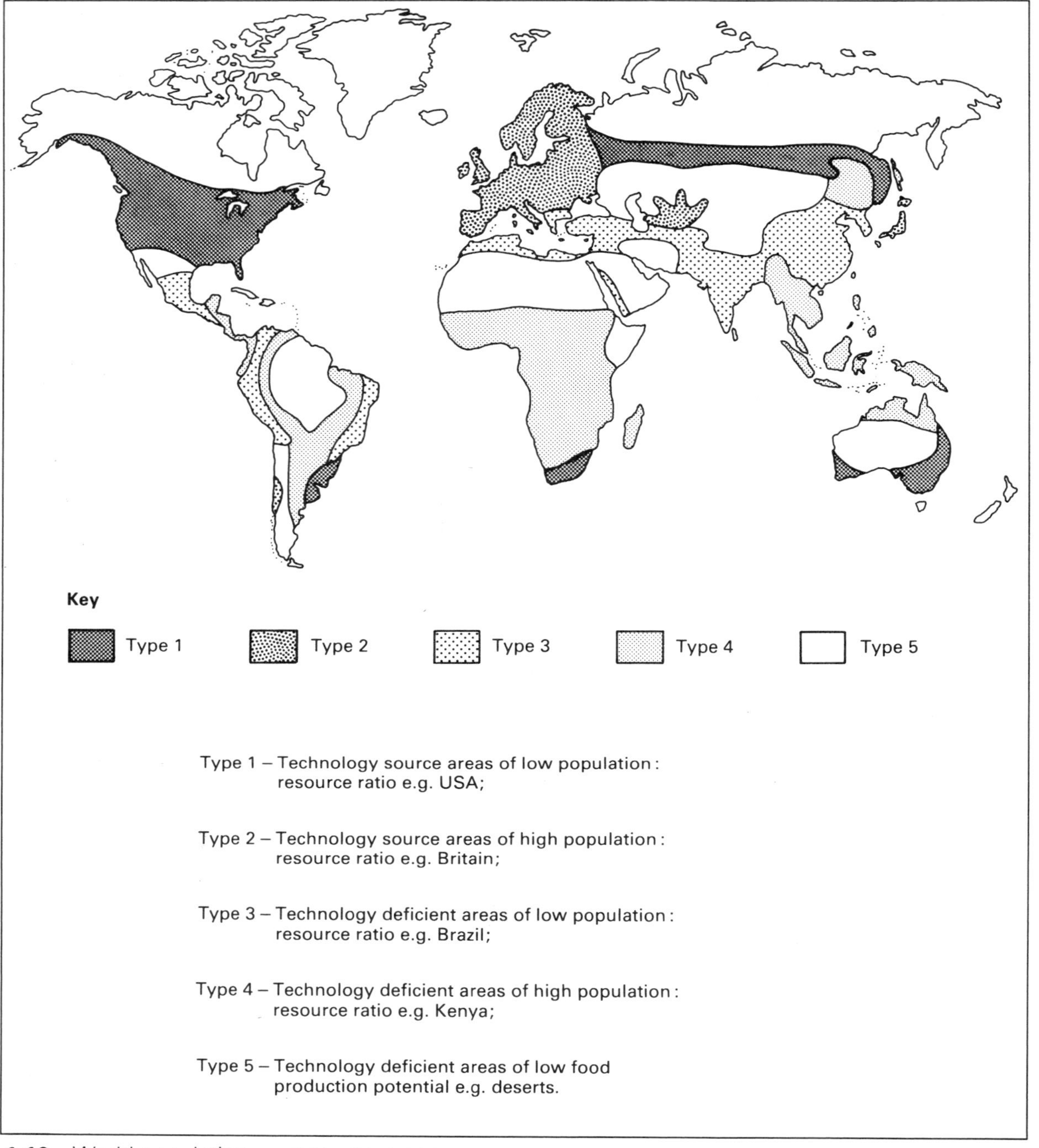

1.10 World population — resource types

5. Outline the factors which could influence projected world population growth rates into the twenty-first century (see Fig. 1.7). Your answer should make specific reference to land and/or water resources wherever appropriate.

6. a) What types of landscape could be included within the category land which 'could be brought into cultivation' as depicted in Fig. 1.8?
   b) What factors will dictate the future use of such types of landscape?

7. Describe and account for the distribution pattern of different population-resource types shown in Fig. 1.10.

2
Climate

Introduction

In order to begin to understand how the Earth's land and water resources are distributed and how they are used by people, it is necessary to grasp certain basic concepts associated with climate, vegetation and soils, and the inter-relationships which exist between them.

The Earth's physical 'system', including climate, vegetation and soils, relies upon the sun as its major source of energy. Rather less than half of the total incoming solar radiation or **insolation** which reaches our outer atmosphere from the sun actually penetrates to the surface of the Earth, the rest being lost immediately in a variety of different ways (Fig. 2.1). Eventually almost all of the energy gained from insolation is radiated back into space, a balancing process which is known as the **'heat budget'**. It is the transfer of heat energy received at the surface which gives rise to the great variety of climate and weather conditions experienced throughout the world.

The fact that 71% of the earth's surface is covered in water, whereas only 29% is land, has a crucial effect on the heat transfer process. This is because water acts as a very efficient store of heat, warming up much more slowly than land and heating to much greater depths. In fact, more than five times as much heat energy is required to raise the temperature of a given volume of sea water by 1°C than is true of the same volume of land.

Constant redistribution of the heat 'stored' within the oceans takes place due to the flow of ocean currents. These are created as a result of the sun heating the sea (and land) in equatorial regions more directly than at higher latitudes nearer the poles (see Fig. 2.2). This causes these waters to expand so the surface in these areas rises slightly higher than seas closer to the poles, with a consequent outflow of warmed water from equatorial regions. The heavier, colder water in polar regions compensates for the movement of warmer water by flowing towards the Equator creating a circulatory system. This is distorted by the Earth's rotation and the distribution of continents to produce the pattern of ocean currents we find today, shown in Fig. 2.3.

The degree of absorption of insolation into the earth's land surface varies according to what is to be found there. For example, like the oceans, forests absorb almost all of the insolation which strikes them, as they are generally dark in colour. The snow-covered polar regions, on the other hand, reflect almost all of the insolation which strikes them.

2.1 The heat budget

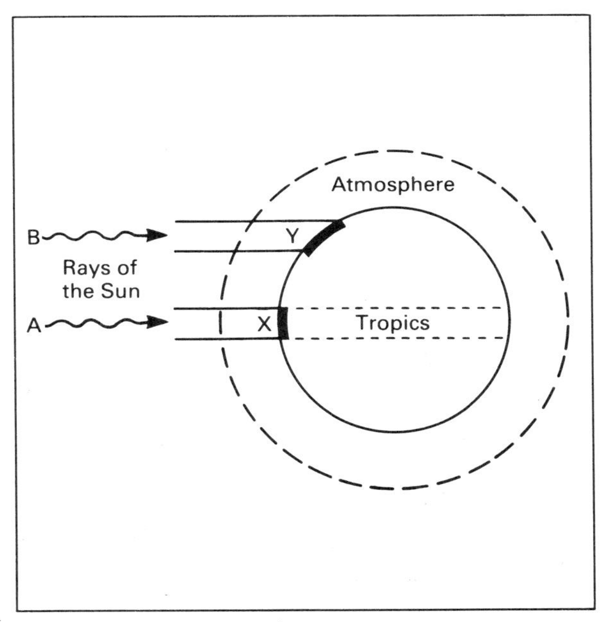

2.2 Effects of latitude on temperature

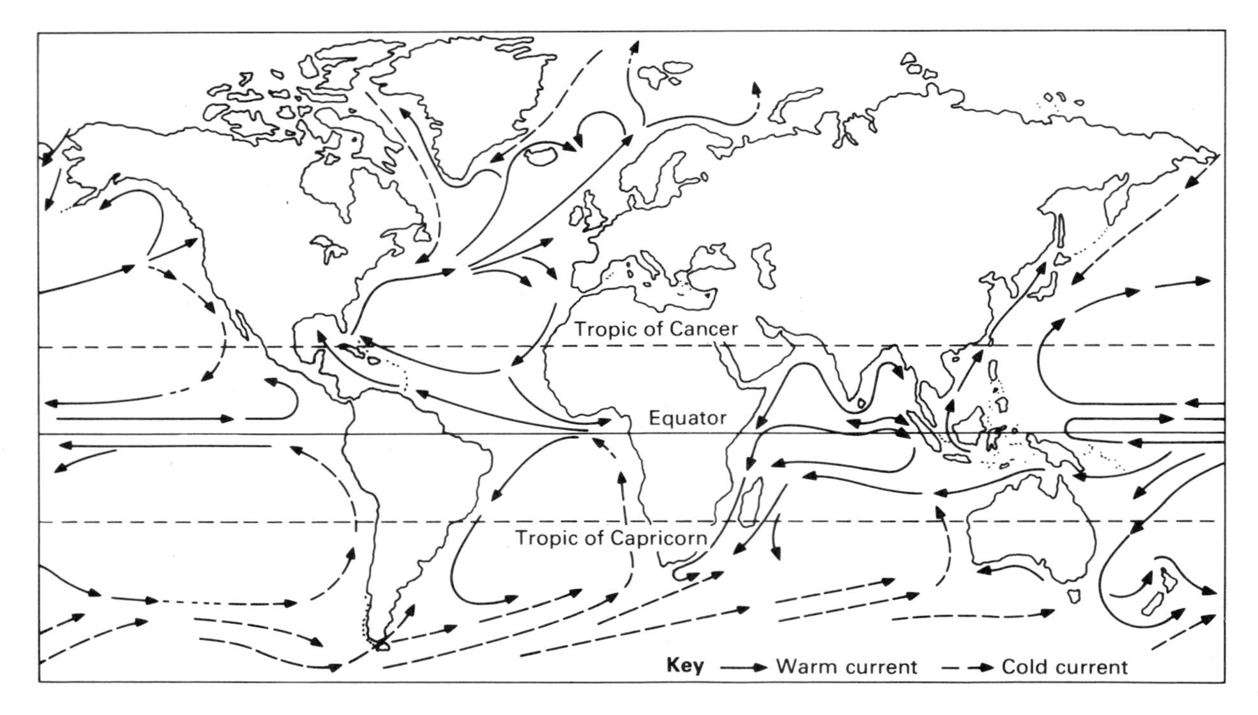

2.3 World ocean currents

Temperature

The atmosphere itself is not heated directly by insolation or the sun's rays; rather it is heated from below by the warmed surface of the Earth. The lower levels of the atmosphere are heated by **conduction**, that is through the air making contact with the Earth's surface, and the upper levels by **convection**, or warm currents of air.

The actual temperatures experienced at any point on the Earth's surface can be affected by a variety of different factors. Certain of these were alluded to earlier in this chapter but now require to be referred to in more detail.

Latitude

In general, average temperatures decrease from the Equator to the poles. This is because the sun heats the Earth's surface most effectively when it shines from directly overhead (see A on Fig. 2.2). This occurs in the region between the tropics. Outside the tropics, the sun's rays tend to be dissipated rather more as a result of travelling a greater distance through the atmosphere (see B on Fig. 2.2) and to be dispersed over a greater surface area than within the tropics (see X and Y on Fig. 2.2). In temperate and polar latitudes, the reduced heating effect of less direct sun's rays is partly compensated for in summer by a longer day and exposure to insolation.

Altitude

One of the main reasons why outgoing radiation does not escape more rapidly into space is because of water vapour and dust particles in the air which create what is known as the **'greenhouse effect'** and act as a barrier. Rising higher and higher into the atmosphere, the air becomes increasingly rarified and the density of water vapour and dust particles decreases resulting in increased heat loss and colder air. It is estimated that average temperatures fall by approximately 1°C with every 150 metres of ascent.

Mountain ranges

In certain areas of the world, the existence of high ranges of mountains acts as a formidable barrier to the free circulation of air in the lower reaches of the atmosphere. The Himalayas, for example, prevent the effects of the monsoon conditions which prevail over the Indian sub-continent extending further north into the interior of Asia and prevent the worst, extremely cold, effects of the anticyclonic winter conditions in central Asia from penetrating south. Similarly the Western Cordillera (including the Rocky Mountains) of North America prevents the intrusion of the westerly maritime influence of the Pacific into the heartland of the Prairies and Great Plains.

Aspect

In localised areas in temperate latitudes (where the sun's rays are less direct than in the tropics), both in the northern and southern hemispheres, **aspect** (the direction in which a slope faces), can also have an affect on temperature. In temperate latitudes in the northern hemisphere, temperatures on south-facing slopes can be significantly increased while the same is true for north-facing slopes in the southern hemisphere.

Distance from the sea

As previously described in this chapter (see page 9), the sea heats up and cools down much more slowly than the land. The effects of this phenomenon are felt most noticeably in temperate latitudes where the warming maritime influence of the sea particularly affects coastal regions in winter. In general the sea can be said to have a 'moderating influence', and to lessen extremes of temperature at all times of the year on coastal areas.

On the other hand, regions deep within the interior of continent land masses experience almost exactly the opposite effect, which is known as **'continentality'**. This results in rapid warming in summer and cooling in winter, causing pronounced extremes of temperature.

Ocean currents

These (Fig. 2.3) have a particular influence on temperature outside of the tropics, particularly where **onshore winds** carry the influence of warm currents towards coastal regions in winter (e.g. the Westerlies over the warm North Atlantic Drift towards North-West Europe). Cold currents obviously have a cooling influence on nearby coasts but generally have a lesser effect than warm currents due to the fact that they often flow below **offshore winds**.

In certain situations, local winds can also have a profound influence upon temperature and significantly affect microclimates e.g. the warming influence of the Fohn and the Chinook on the leeward sides of the Alps and Rockies respectively.

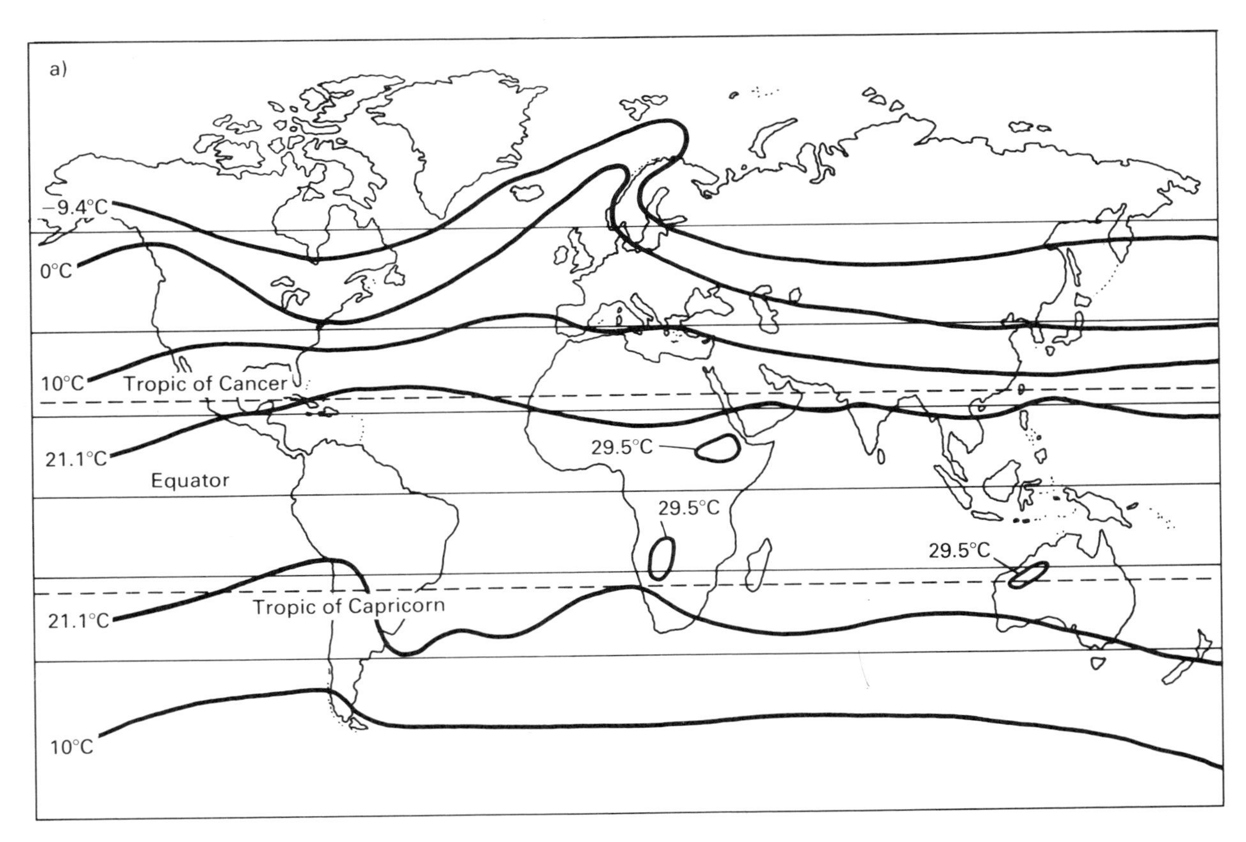

2.4a World January temperatures

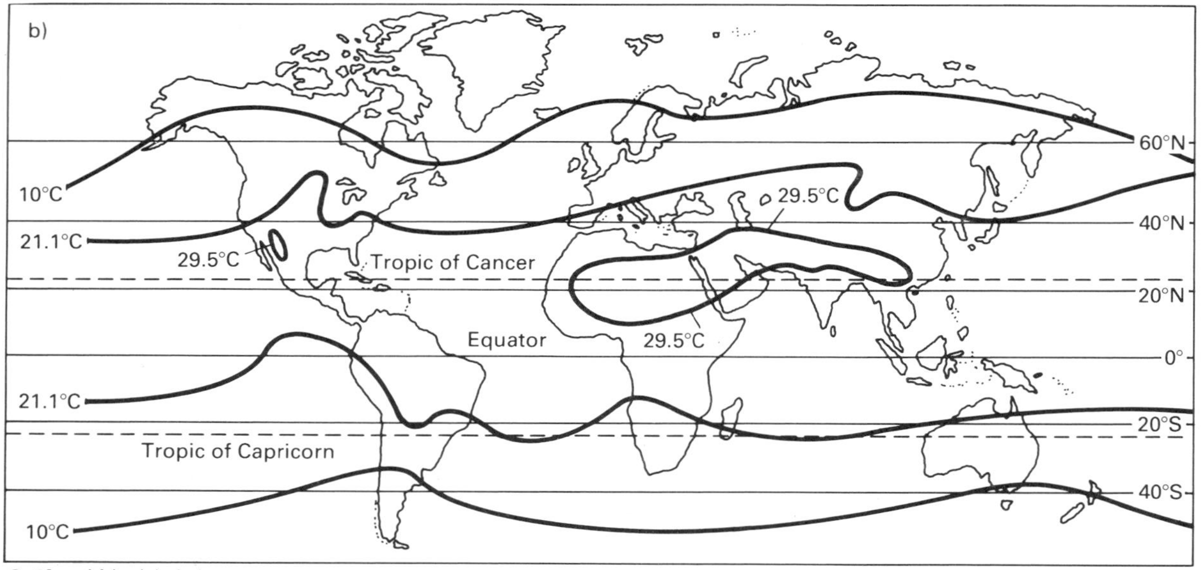

2.4b World July temperatures

Clouds

The presence or absence of clouds in the atmosphere over different parts of the Earth's surface can have a significant bearing on temperature. Clouds have the effect of reducing both the amount of insolation which reaches the surface of the Earth and of outgoing radiation from the Earth's surface. As a result, tropical rain forests with their dense cloud cover have very little range of temperature whereas the hot deserts, which have comparatively little cloud cover, have both a high **diurnal** and annual temperature range.

Maps which show worldwide distribution of temperature reveal how all of these factors interact to produce considerable variations at different times of the year (see Figs. 2.4a and 2.4b). On these maps **isotherms** (lines which join places with the same temperatures), are used to show these variations.

Pressure and winds

Differential heating of the Earth's surface from the Equator to the poles creates unequal pressure patterns in different parts of the atmosphere. This results from the fact that air expands, becomes less dense and rises when it is heated. As the rising air moves up into the atmosphere, it leaves a surface area of low pressure behind it — as less air is found there than previously. Eventually, this surface low pressure centre will be 'infilled' by the movement inwards of air from surrounding higher pressure areas and the rising mass of warmed air will stop rising when it reaches air of similar pressure, when it will start to cool and descend. We thus have the beginnings of both a vertical and a horizontal circulatory system. The horizontal movement of air from high towards low pressure is, of course, known to us all as a wind. How the movements described above transfer to the macro scale, on a world stage, is illustrated in Fig. 2.5.

Pressure belts

In an ideal situation, and as Fig. 2.5 shows, at the Equator heated air rises leaving a low pressure area which is known as the Doldrums. This heated air then flows polewards, cooling as it moves, prior to descending towards the tropics and creating the belt of sub-tropical high pressure. These sub-tropical highs are also the source of air moving along the surface towards the Poles. At the Poles, the low temperatures cause the air to contract and create a zone of high pressure. This dense cold air flows Equatorwards away from the area of high pressure and is replaced by air from the upper atmosphere.

The much simplified picture illustrated by Fig. 2.5 shows the ideal situation at the equinoxes when the sun is overhead at the Equator. This is, however, subject to considerable modification during different seasons of the year by a shift in the pressure belts. By late June, for example, when the sun is overhead at the Tropic of Cancer, the Doldrums low pressure belt will have moved significantly northwards from the Equator with a resultant shift of the other belts in the northern hemisphere. Similarly, in late December, when the sun is overhead at the Tropic of Capricorn, the belts will have moved southwards.

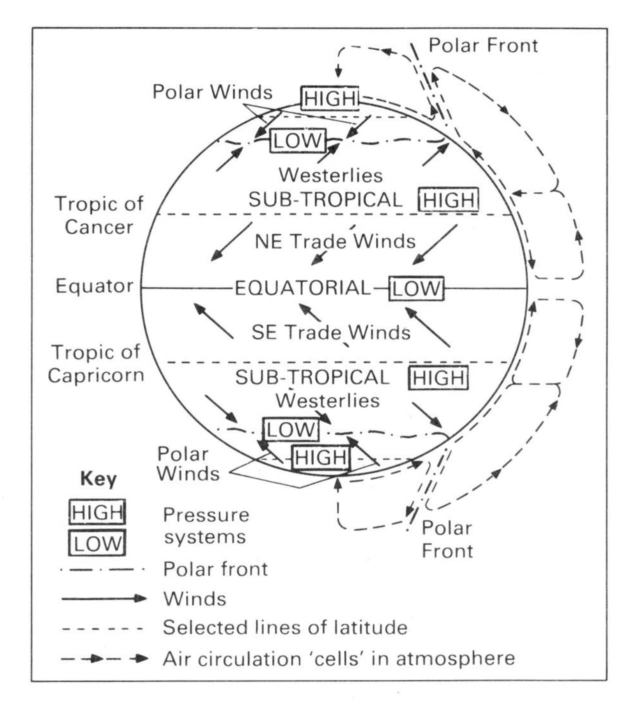

2.5 World pressure and wind patterns

Apart from the seasons, the Earth's rotation also has an affect on pressure, tending to deflect air from the poles towards the Equator and on the wind systems which at the surface result from the flow of air from high to low pressure areas down the so-called 'pressure gradient'. In the northern hemisphere, the Earth's rotation tends to deflect winds to the right and in the southern hemisphere towards the left (see Fig. 2.5). Within each hemisphere, three different sets of wind systems can be found:

— the equatorial systems (trade winds) from the Equator to 30°N and S approx.
— the tropical systems (westerlies) from 30 to 60°N and S approx.
— the polar systems (polar winds) from 60 to 90°N and S approx.

The other major factor which affects pressure belts and wind systems is the pattern of distribution of land and sea. This is particularly true in South-East Asia, where monsoon winds completely distort the normal planetary wind pattern for such latitudes, and over the large continental land masses where high pressure conditions and outblowing winds often develop over the interiors in winter and low pressure conditions with inblowing winds in summer.

1. Describe and explain the pattern of the ocean currents in the Atlantic Ocean shown in Fig. 2.3.

	Maximum average monthly temperature	Minimum average monthly temperature	Temperature range
Station A	16°C	8°C	8°C
Station B	24°C	−3°C	27°C
Station C	20°C	1°C	19°C

2. a) Explain the differences in temperatures experienced at the three climate stations above which all lie near to the 50°N line of latitude in Europe.
   b) With the help of an atlas, identify stations A, B, and C from the following list: Berlin, Warsaw, London.
   Give reasons to support your answers.
3. Study Fig. 2.4a and 2.4b. Suggest why the 21.1°C isotherm over the southern hemisphere takes a southerly bend over each land mass.
4. a) Draw a simple annotated diagram to illustrate the pressure belts and pattern of air movement over the northern hemisphere in July and January.
   b) Briefly explain the differences between the two diagrams.
5. a) In general terms, describe the pattern of the world's wind systems.
   b) Apart from the pressure belts, what other factors affect world wind systems and how does this show itself in reality?

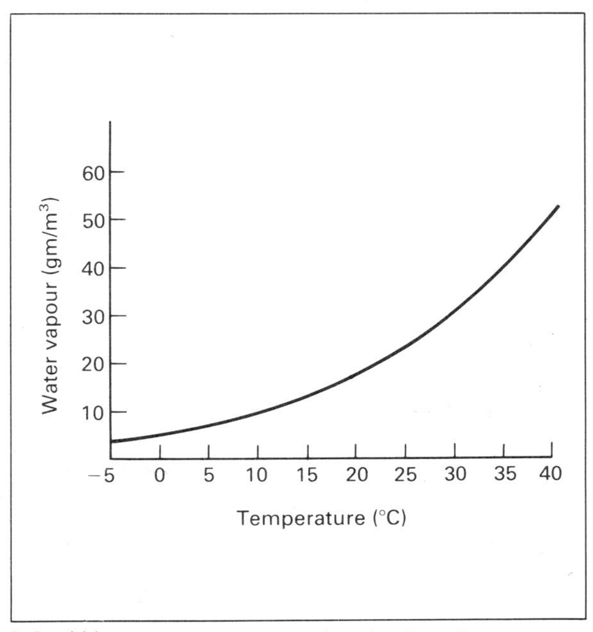

2.6 Water vapour saturation in the air at different temperatures

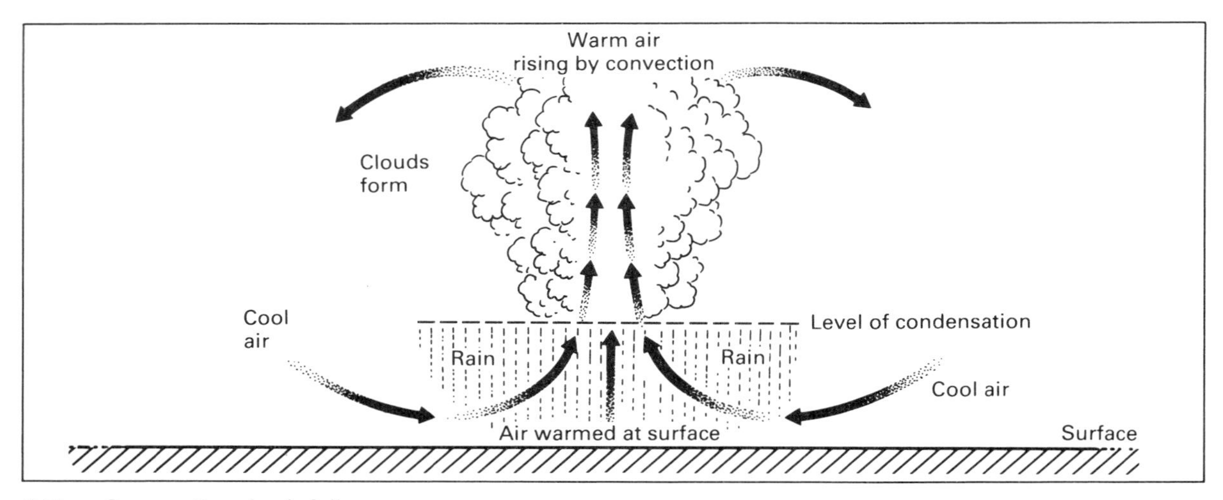

2.7a Convectional rainfall

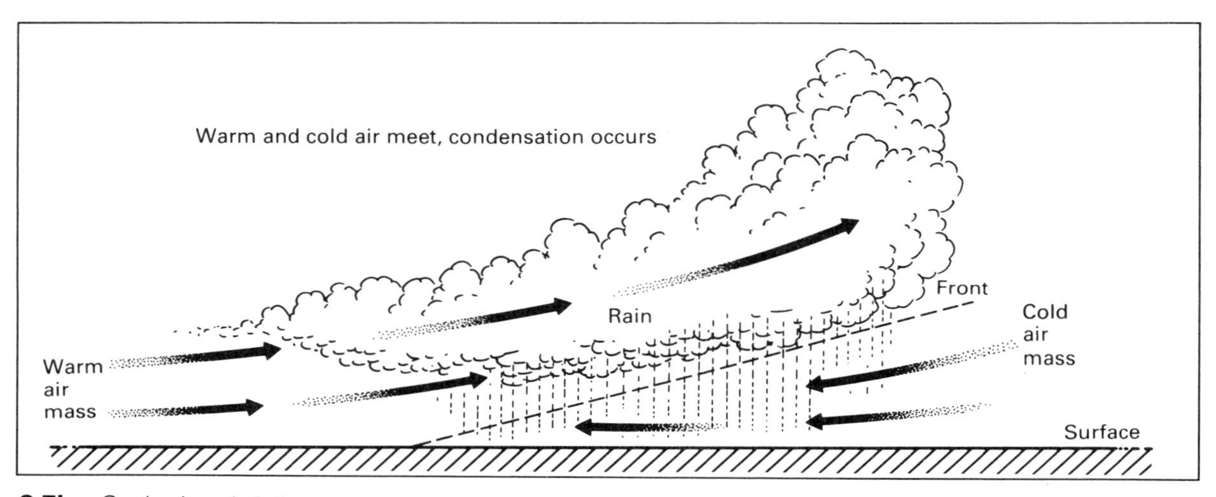

2.7b Cyclonic rainfall

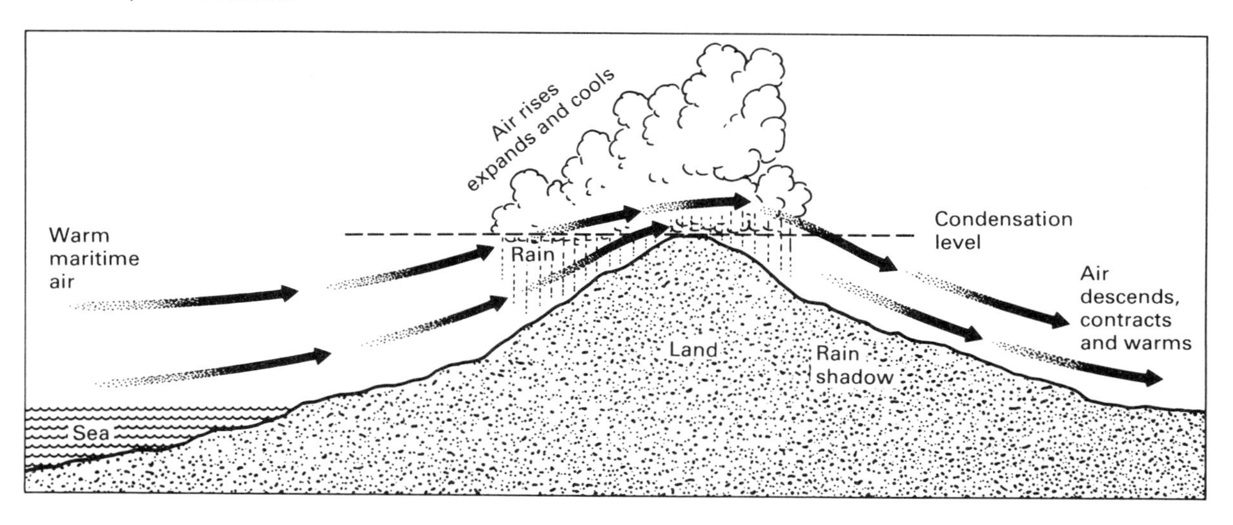

2.7c Relief rainfall

Precipitation

Water vapour is present in gaseous form in all of the air found in the Earth's atmosphere and plays a very important role in world climate. The amount of water vapour present in the air varies considerably from place to place as warm air has a much greater capacity to hold water vapour than cold air (see Fig. 2.6). Precipitation, in one of its forms, will occur when rising warm air begins to cool and water vapour gradually condenses as tiny droplets on dust particles in the atmosphere. The stage at which this is reached, when the air becomes saturated with water vapour, is known as the **'dew point'** temperature. It is at this point that clouds, mist or fog may result and that snow, hail, sleet or rain will be likely to follow if cooling and condensation continues.

Types of rainfall

As we have seen, precipitation occurs when air is cooled, and one of the ways in which this can occur is when warmed air rises freely into the atmosphere, resulting in **convectional rainfall** (Fig. 2.7a). Precipitation can also occur at times when warmed air is forced into contact with cold air, such as when warm and cold air masses meet at a **front**, resulting in **cyclonic rainfall** (see Fig. 2.7b) or when a mass of warm air is forced to rise over a range of mountains, resulting in **relief** or **orographic rainfall** (Fig. 2.7c). Similarly, when warm air is blown over a cold sea, mist will form and when warm air is blown over cold land a fog will form.

The water (or hydrological) cycle

The 71% of the Earth's surface which is water absorbs large amounts of energy in the form of insolation from the sun. It is this 'store' of energy which fuels the **water cycle** (Fig. 2.8), the transfer of water between the Earth's atmosphere, **hydrosphere, biosphere** and **lithosphere**. Although 71% of the Earth's surface is water, 97% of this is salt water found in the oceans and seas. The remaining 3% is fresh water but three-quarters of that is

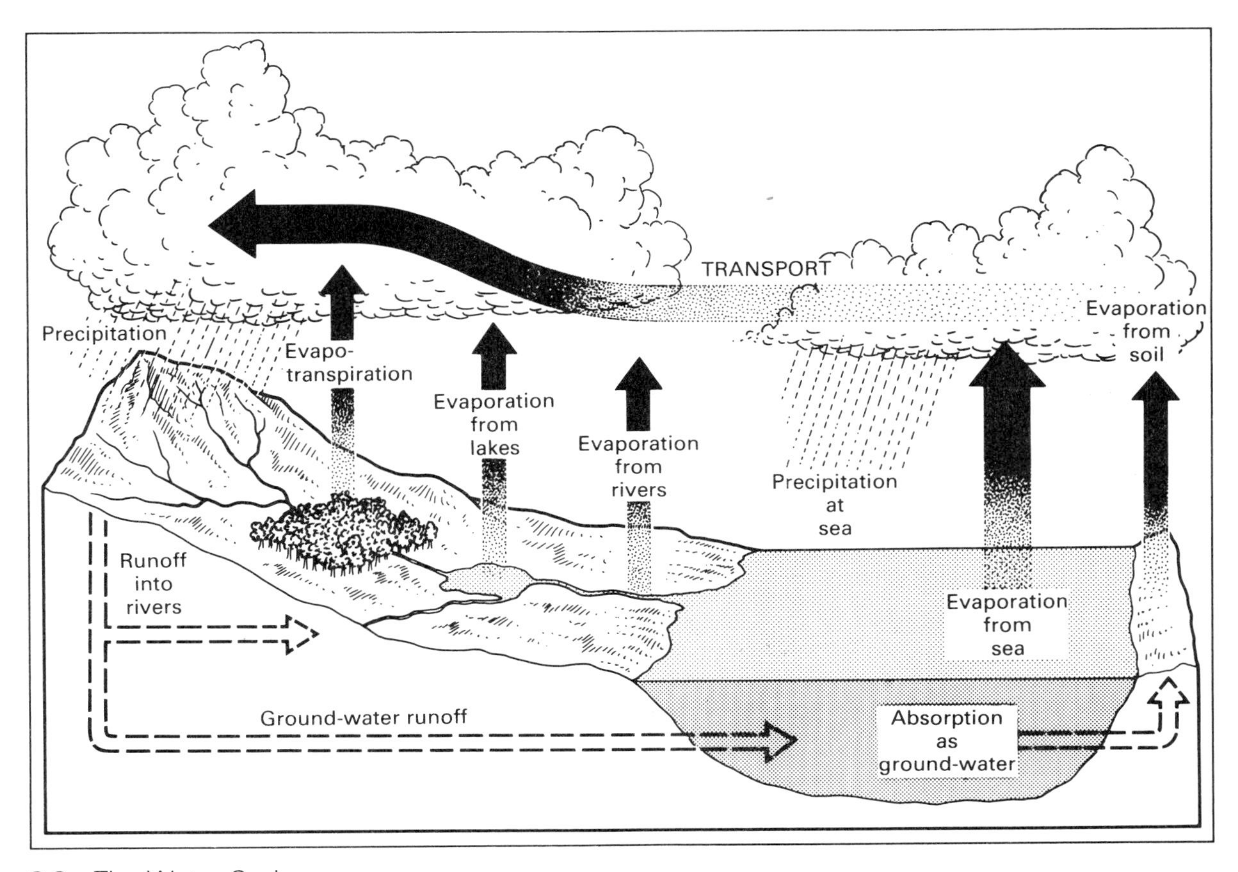

2.8 The Water Cycle

frozen into the polar ice-caps.This means that only 0.75% of the Earth's water is available in the short-term for transfer through the water cycle, and much of this not actually surface water but ground-water instead. As can be seen in Fig. 2.8, the basic processes involved in the water cycle are:
— evaporation — of water from the oceans
— transportation — of water vapour over land
— condensation — of water vapour into liquid, droplet, form due to air being forced to rise as a result of convection, relief or frontal activity
— precipitation — of water onto or into the ground
— run-off/evaporation/evapotranspiration — of water from on or below the surface, from lakes and rivers and from plants.

Later in this book we look at the various ways in which people interfere with the water cycle (see chapter 5).

World rainfall patterns

Although the shift of the pressure belts at different times of the year does affect distribution of rainfall in certain areas of the world, it is still possible to identify certain general patterns. For example the regions of the world which tend to be wet all year round lie within:
— the equatorial zone, due to high convectional rainfall
— the temperate zone, especially on the **western margins of continents** with prevailing westerly onshore winds, due to high cyclonic and/or relief rainfall.

Other regions which experience marked differences with the seasons, include:
— the monsoon lands (see chapter 3) of southern and eastern Asia, due to onshore, rain bearing winds during the wet season and offshore winds during the dry season
— the Mediterranean lands and savannas (see chapter 3), due to the shift of the pressure belts.

A further set of regions experience very low precipitation at all times of the year. These include:
— the hot deserts (see chapter 3), due to the fact that the prevailing winds are offshore (the trades)
— the interior of the Eurasian and North American land masses, due to the lack of rain bearing winds.

Classifying world climates

Many eminent geographers have proposed different ways of classifying world climates in the past, with varying degrees of complexity. For our purposes it is probably best that we classify world climate as simply as possible through the use of two 'variables', the basic elements of climate we have all worked with regularly: temperature and rainfall. Initially it is useful to remind ourselves that the Earth can be subdivided into five broad climatic 'belts': the tropical belt, two temperate belts and two polar belts. Thereafter it is useful to subdivide the land masses within the temperate belts in two ways:
— latitudinally, into 'warm' and 'cool' temperate
— longitudinally, into eastern margin, western margin and continental interior.

Fig. 2.9a shows twelve different climate zones and Fig. 2.9b attempts to summarise the characteristics of each of these and quote relevant examples.

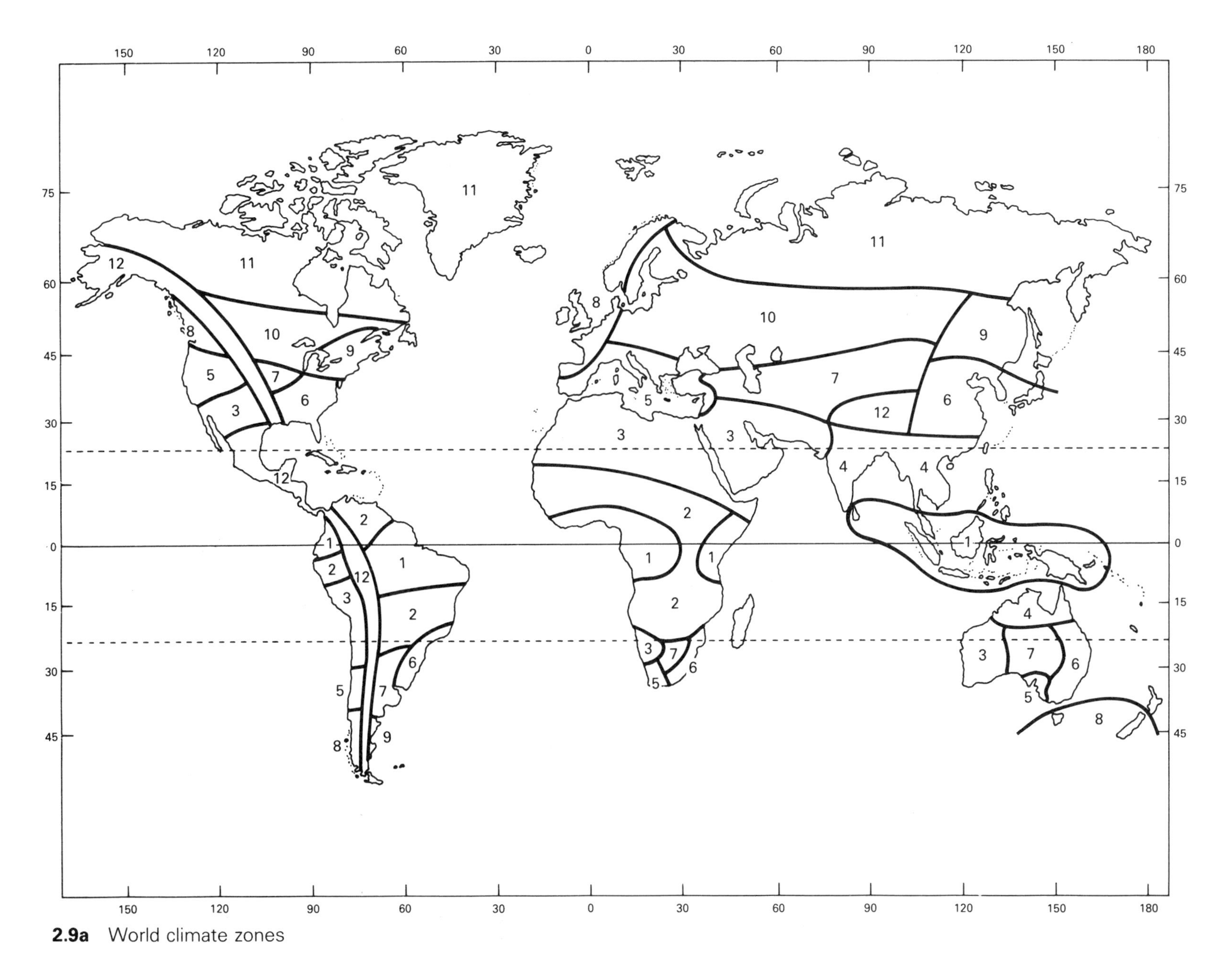

2.9a World climate zones

Zone	Climate characteristics	Reasons	Example	Temperature (°C)			Rainfall (mm)	
				Max	Min	Range	Annual total	Distribution
ALTITUDE								
12. Mountain	Patterns vary greatly from place to place. Aspect and local winds play a part.	Temperatures decrease on average by 1°C for every 150 metres of ascent						
Polar (90°)								
11. Arctic	Very cold temperatures in winter, cool summers. Precipitation largely in form of snow	Low levels of insolation throughout year	Aklavik (Canada)	14	−28	42	220	Summer rain
Cool temperate								
10. Interior	Very large temperature range, very low sub-zero temperatures. Largely summer rainfall	Continentality causes temperature extremes, convectional rainfall in summer	Regina (Canada)	18	−18	36	380	Summer rain
9. Eastern margin	Greater temperature range than 8 but similar all year round rainfall pattern	Lower winter temperatures due to cold outblowing winds from interior	St. Johns (Canada)	17	−4	21	1360	All year
8. Western margin	Moderate temperatures, equable range precipitation throughout year	Moderating maritime influence and prevailing Westerlies all year round	Victoria (Canada)	16	4	12	750	All year
Warm temperate								
7. Interior	Large temperature range, warm summers, cold winters. Rainfall mostly in summer 6 months	Continentality causes great range, low pressure predominant in summer, convectional rainfall	St Louis (USA)	26	0	26	1000	Summer rain
6. Eastern margin	Hot, wet 'tropical type' summer; mild, moist winters (colder & drier in China)	Seasonal wind reversal; onshore trades in summer, offshore Westerlies in winter	Charleston (USA)	27	10	17	1200	Summer rain
5. Western margin (Mediterranean)	Hot, dry summers with cloudless skies, generally warm wet winters	Belt of sub-tropical highs in summer and warm Trade winds, Westerlies in winter	Rome (Italy)	25	7	18	850	Winter rain
Tropical								
4. Monsoon	Fairly high temperatures, moderate range. Marked summer 6 months wet season/ winter 6 months dry	Summer-onshore winds towards continental 'Low' interior, winter reversal	Bombay (India)	30	24	6	1800	Summer rain
3. Hot desert	Very high maximum temperatures in summer but high diurnal range. Little rainfall	High pressure predominant, long hours of sunshine, cloudless skies. Prevailing offshore winds	Ain Salah (Algeria)	37	13	24	120	Infrequent (but negligible)
2. Savanna	Fairly high temperatures, larger range than 1. Marked summer wet season/winters dry.	Still high level of insolation, pressure belt shift creates summer low. Offshore trades in winter	Kayes (Mali)	34	23	11	750	Summer rain
1. Equatorial (0°)	Constant very high temperatures all year, small range; very high rainfall	High levels of insolation. Equatorial low pressure belt. Daily convectional rainfall	Singapore	28	26	2	2500	All year

LATITUDE

6. Equatorial belt, temperate belt, polar belt. Above which of these three climate belts will air have the greatest potential to carry water vapour? Explain why.

7. a) With reference to Figs. 2.2, 2.5, 2.7a, b and c and with the help of an atlas map, identify two examples of parts of the world where each of the three different types of precipitation are likely to occur. Give reasons for your answer in each case.

   b) Identify and list the stages which all three precipitation 'types' have in common.

8. Account for the fact that only 0.75% of the Earth's water resources are available for short-term human use.

9. Study the rainfall statistics below and attempt to identify the region of the world within which each climate station is located. Give reasons for your answer in each case.

10. Explain the differences between rainfall distribution in tropical grasslands and monsoon lands.

11. Compare and contrast the general climatic conditions experienced in two of the following three pairs of climate zones. Suggest reasons for the similarities and differences.
— cool temperate western margin/warm temperate western margin
— cool temperate interior margin/warm temperate interior margin
— cool temperate eastern margin/warm temperate eastern margin.

Month	J	F	M	A	M	J	J	A	S	O	N	D	
Station A	10	10	8	3	2	2	5	15	10	8	5	12	Northern Hemisphere
Station B	113	96	65	54	37	15	9	15	45	93	107	132	Northern Hemisphere
Station C	3	5	7	51	308	479	581	528	393	181	67	12	Northern Hemisphere

2.9b General characteristics of world climate zones

3

Vegetation and bio-climatic zones

Vegetation

There are relatively few areas on the land surface of the Earth where the environment is so hostile that no growth of vegetation is possible. Perhaps the only regions where this is true are on the peaks of high mountains and on the ice-caps around the poles. Practically everywhere else vegetation in some form or another is to be found.

Before plant growth will take place, five 'elements' must interact: heat and light (from insolation), carbon dioxide (from the air) and water and mineral salts (both taken in via roots from the soil). The absence or relative scarcity of any one of these elements for any length of time can reduce or temporarily suspend plant growth. In the presence of all five elements, the process of **photosynthesis** continuously takes place, whereby carbon dioxide taken in through the leaves combines with water and mineral salts to produce the food which promotes growth. The surplus water created in this way is then lost via the leaves into the atmosphere in a process known as **transpiration**.

The infinite variety of vegetation types found in different areas of the world is controlled in large part by two aspects of climate: temperature and precipitation. As we all know, average temperatures tend to decrease as degree of latitude increases. Given that growing point temperature is 6°C (below which no plant growth normally takes place), the tropical belt, where average temperatures constantly exceed 6°C, has the potential for all-year-round vegetation growth. In temperate regions, potential for plant growth tends to be of a more seasonal nature as average temperatures fall below 6°C for several months of the year. Around the poles, where average temperatures rarely exceed 6°C and the ground is permanently ice or snow-covered, no vegetation

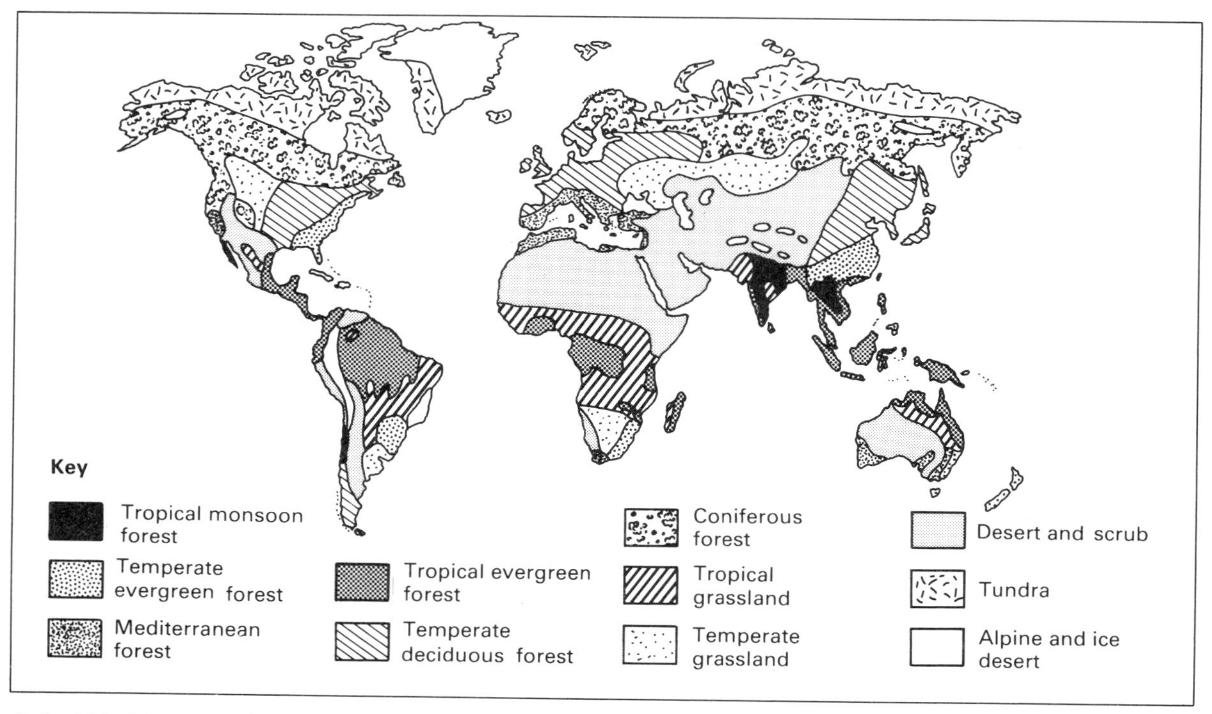

3.1 World vegetation zones

is to be found. Despite the fact that the tropical belt, and the temperate belt at certain times of the year, have the potential for vigorous plant growth due to more than adequate average temperatures, the lack of sufficient moisture in certain regions throughout the year and in others during particular seasons, virtually precludes the continuous growth of vegetation. In general, therefore, rainfall tends to determine the vegetation type, e.g. high rainfall — forest; little rainfall — grassland; sparse rainfall — desert or semi-desert; whereas temperature can often be said to play a part in which plant varieties are to be found, e.g. the different kinds of forest and tree species to be found at low latitudes in contrast to mid-latitudes.

The vegetation types which have evolved through time in different regions (Fig. 3.1) are not just adapted to withstand normal conditions however, they also require to be capable of resisting extremes of various sorts. In dry environments, for example, many plants show drought-resistant or **xerophytic** adaptation, which allows them to survive without water for years when necessary.

In different regions of the world, the natural vegetation to be found is therefore a direct **biotic** response to specific climatic and other environmental conditions. Each of these regions has clear characteristics, both in terms of natural vegetation and climate, which allow us to describe them as **bio-climatic zones** or **biomes**. If it were not for human influence, these zones would remain as truly natural landscapes, but in reality human activity has had a marked effect, e.g. the drastic reduction in area of tropical rain forest, the use of temperate grasslands for pastoral and arable farming, and attempts at 'turning the desert green'.

1. By means of an annotated sketch, attempt to summarise the environmental conditions required for plant growth to take place.

2. Explain the part played by a) temperature, and b) precipitation in determining vegetation types in different areas of the world.

3. Using two bioclimatic zones as examples, explain how 'the natural vegetation to be found is a direct biotic response to specific climatic and other environmental conditions'.

4. a) Identify the bioclimatic zones within which plant growth occurs: i) all year round, ii) for the majority of months of the year and iii) in relatively few months of the year (refer to Fig. 2.9b) on p. 18.
   b) Choose one bio-climatic zone identified for i) and iii) above and describe one specific way in which vegetation has adapted in each zone.

Bio-climatic zones

The bio-climatic zones described later in this chapter are derived from the maps of world climate and vegetation (see Figs. 2.9a p. 17 and 3.1 respectively) but in a simplified form. Each zone has been dealt with individually in terms of distribution and main climate and vegetation characteristics. It should be borne in mind, however, that these zones gradually merge into each other rather than one abruptly stopping and another starting.

3.2 Tropical rainforest, Sarawak, Malaysia

Zone 1: tropical rain forests

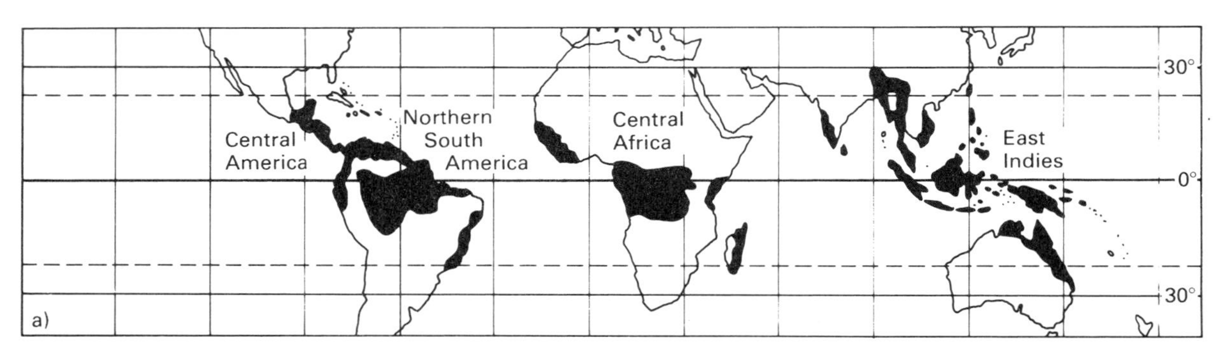

3.3a Distribution of tropical rainforest

Climate

1. Temperature
   a) Very high (25°C) throughout year, with small range (1–5°C).
   b) Diurnal range of temperature sometimes larger than annual range.
   c) Marked lack of seasonality.
2. Rainfall
   a) Very high rainfall (> 2000 mm), usually fairly evenly distributed throughout year.
   b) Monotonous weather pattern every day, convectional thunderstorms bringing torrential rainfall most afternoons.
3. Humidity
   Constantly high, uncomfortable, 'sticky' climate.

Vegetation

1. Combination of high temperatures and rainfall produces luxuriant vegetation growth. Great profusion of plant species.
2. Broadleaved, deciduous trees are found, e.g. hardwoods such as ebony, teak and mahogany. Trees rarely occur in stands. Most branches and foliage near tops of tree.
3. Middle layer of trees form canopy where tree crowns merge.
4. Epiphytic plants such as lianas grow on the trees.

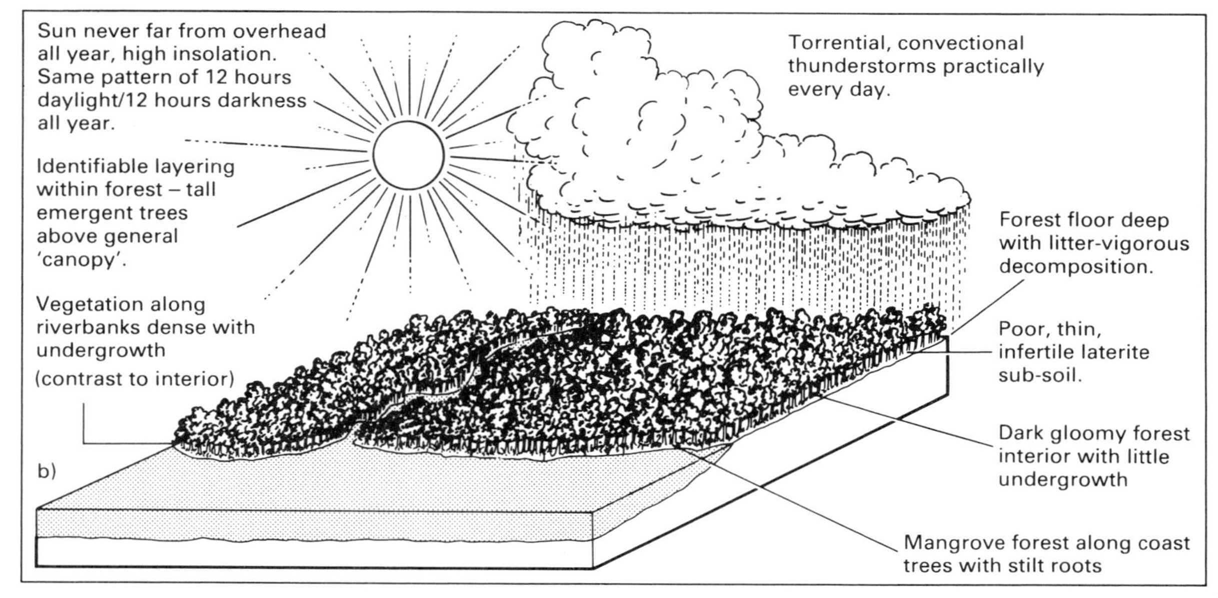

3.3b Summary block diagram of tropical rainforest landscape

Zone 2: tropical grassland

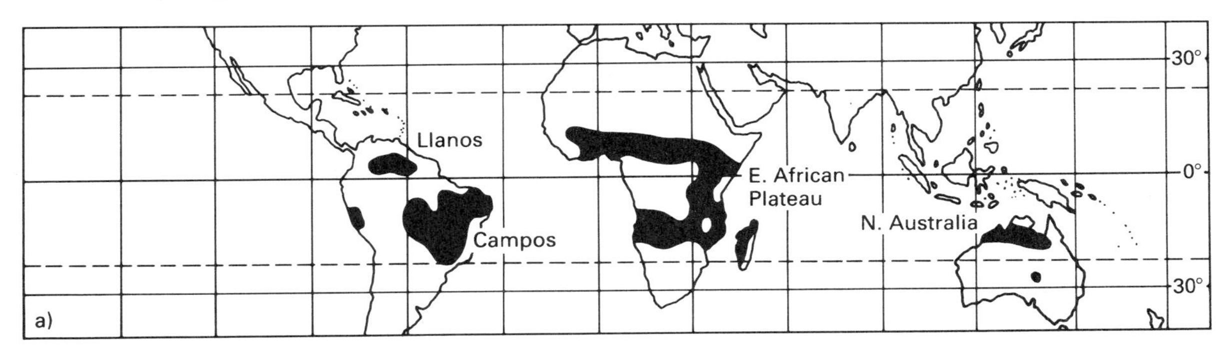

3.4a Distribution of tropical grasslands

Climate

1. Temperature
   a) Small range (8–10°C) but greater than tropical rain forests.
   b) Higher maximum (30°C) than tropical rain forests, but lower minimum (12–14°C), always warm.
   c) Highest temperatures coincide with onset of summer rains.
2. Rainfall
   a) Pronounced summer wet season and winter dry season.
   b) Convectional rainfall creates marked summer maximum.
   c) Total annual rainfall normally considerably less than tropical rainforest.

Vegetation (based upon sub-Saharan West African savanna). Grasses and deciduous trees dominate the savanna landscape, generally showing less prolific growth as latitude and distance from the sea increase. Three main sub-zones are to be found (see diagram):

1. Savanna parkland: twisted, branching, deciduous trees, e.g. baobabs, acacia and eucalyptus, grow fairly close to each other. Beneath the trees, cover grasses, adapted to seed and die back at the start of the dry season, grow.
2. Savanna grassland: trees are less dense and often draw water from an underlying aquifer through long root system. Grasses tend to be tall and coarse in areas of higher precipitation, more sparse in areas with less precipitation.
3. Savanna scrub: vegetation tends to be a discontinuous layer of bushes, e.g. sagebrush and thorns and sparse, dried-up tussocks of grass. This zone has experienced the worst effects of advancing desertification.

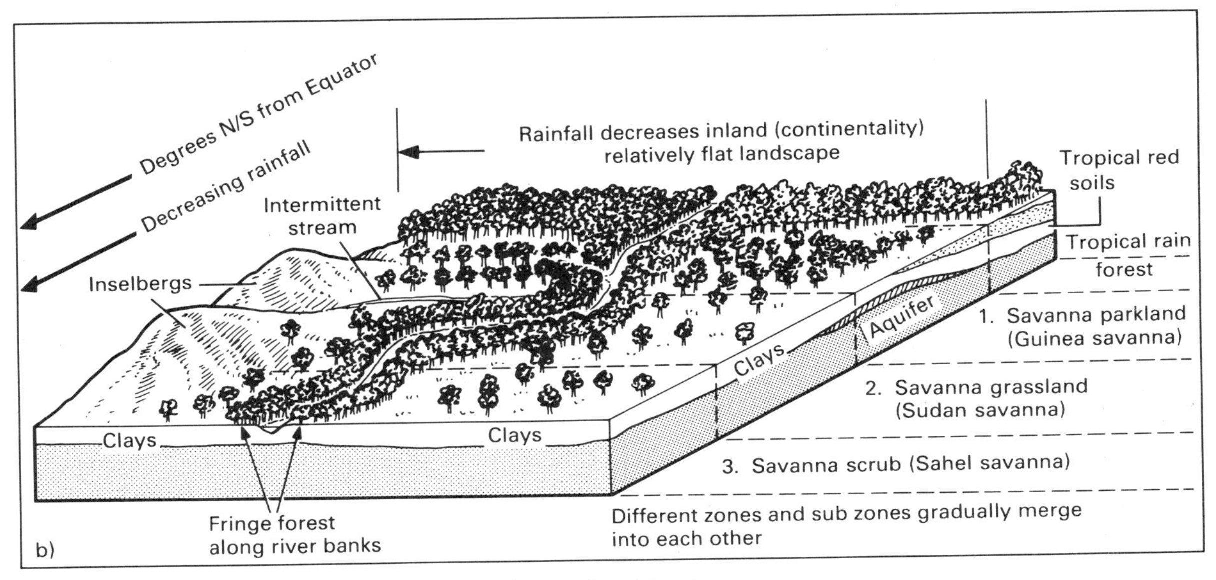

3.4b Summary block diagram of tropical grassland landscape

Zone 3: hot deserts

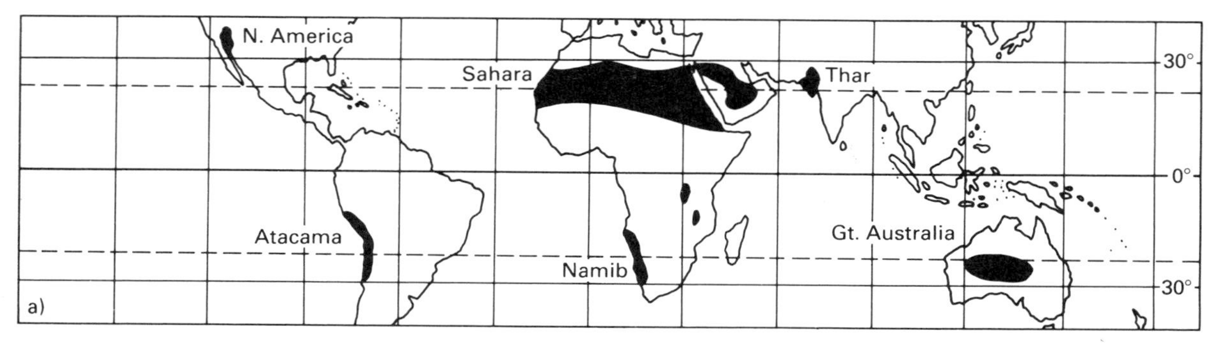

3.5a Distribution of hot desert

Climate

1. Temperature
   a) Very high maxima (35°C approx) during hot season (30°C) but cooler season (15–18°C) also, and fairly high annual range (15–20°C).
   b) Very high diurnal range due to lack of cloud cover.
2. Rainfall
   Zone is very arid, has little and infrequent rain (< 250 mm per annum).
3. Winds
   Can be strong and have a drying effect, create frequent sandstorms.

Vegetation Vegetation tends to be sparse and scattered due to lack of moisture and fast absorption and evaporation when it does occur. Only exception is at oases where groundwater found near surface.

1. Vegetation types, e.g. coarse grasses, thorn bushes, tumbleweed, cacti, all require to lie dormant for long periods between rain and to complete life cycle rapidly when it happens.
2. Plants have adapted in various ways to desert conditions: many have long roots to tap groundwater; some have tough, leathery and waxy skins to reduce water loss; others can conserve water in spongy interiors and lack leaves to reduce transpiration.

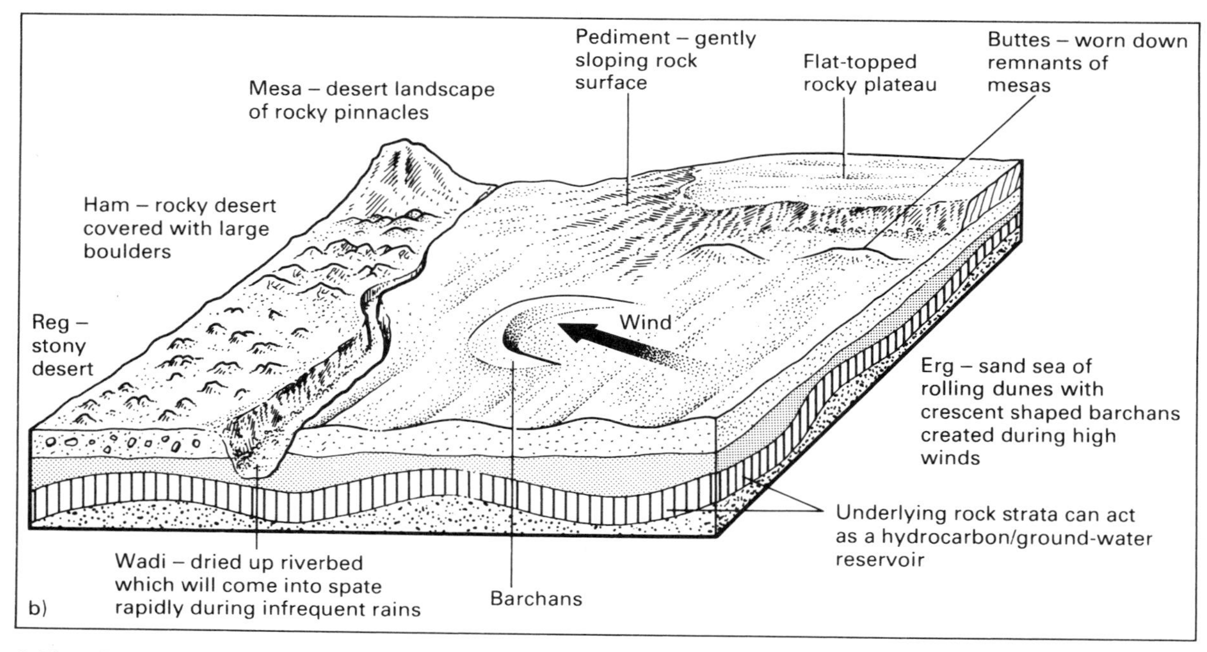

3.5b Summary block diagram of hot desert landscape

Zone 4: monsoon lands

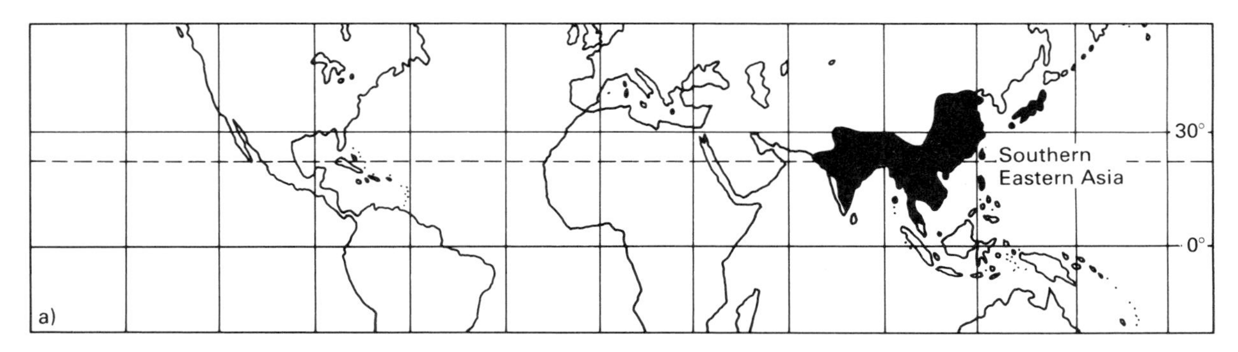

3.6a Distribution of monsoon land

Climate

1. Monsoon winds
   The climate of monsoon lands is largely determined by these seasonal winds. Excessive heating of Asiatic continental interior in summer creates low pressure which sucks in onshore rainbearing winds. Landmass cools during winter and pressure rises, winds switch to offshore.
2. Seasonality
   Over the Indian sub-continent three seasons can be identified:
   a) The rainy season (June to October) when the south-west monsoon prevails and torrential rainfall can occur. Rainfall can exceed 2000 mm per annum.
   b) The cool season (November to January) when the north-east monsoon prevails and little rainfall occurs.
   c) The hot season (February to May), north-east monsoon declines in prominence as season progresses. Temperatures 30°C are not uncommon.

Vegetation As monsoon lands extend from sub-equatorial regions to 35°N (in Japan) and range considerably in height, a great variety of natural vegetation is to be found where it remains in more remote areas. True monsoon evergreen forest contains deciduous hardwood trees which can rise to more than thirty metres in height. In fringe areas, where rainfall is less, the forest is more sparse and thorny bushes e.g. acacia, are interspersed with trees.

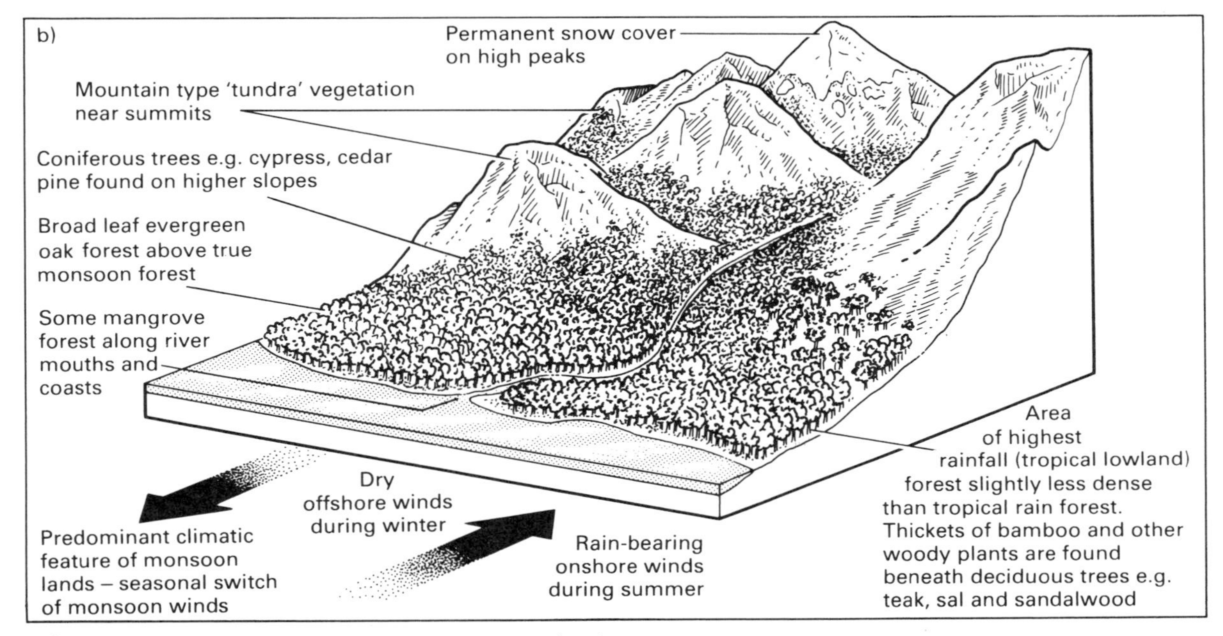

3.6b Summary block diagram of monsoon landscape

Zone 5: Mediterranean lands

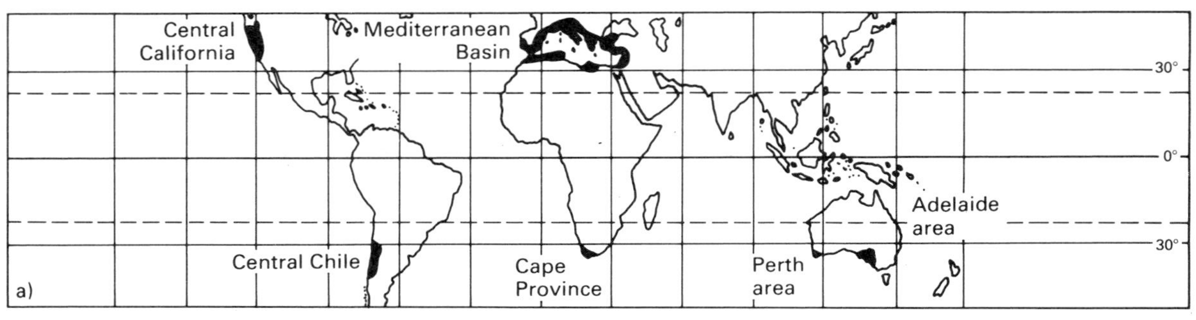

3.7a Distribution of Mediterranean lands

Climate

1. Temperature
   a) Range between 21°C in summer and 6°C in winter.
   b) Cloudless skies with long hours of bright sunshine characterise summer months.
2. Rainfall
   a) In summer, dry offshore trade winds blow, drought conditions prevail.
   b) In winter, wet onshore westerlies can bring up to 500 mm of rain.

Vegetation All Mediterranean vegetation requires to be adapted to survive the summer drought. Most plants are evergreen with small but thick waxy leaves to reduce transpiration.

1. In lower-lying coastal areas, open woodland, e.g. of evergreen and cork oak cypress and cedar trees, used to predominate.
2. On slightly higher sloping areas, conifers such as the Corsican and Aleppo pines are found.
3. 'Maquis' vegetation of evergreen shrubs, e.g. gorse, oleander, thornwoods, laurel, stunted olive and dwarf oak, is found higher up and in areas of lower than average rainfall.
4. In limestone areas, with their dry soils, 'garrigue' vegetation of rosemary broom, lavender and occasional cedars is found.

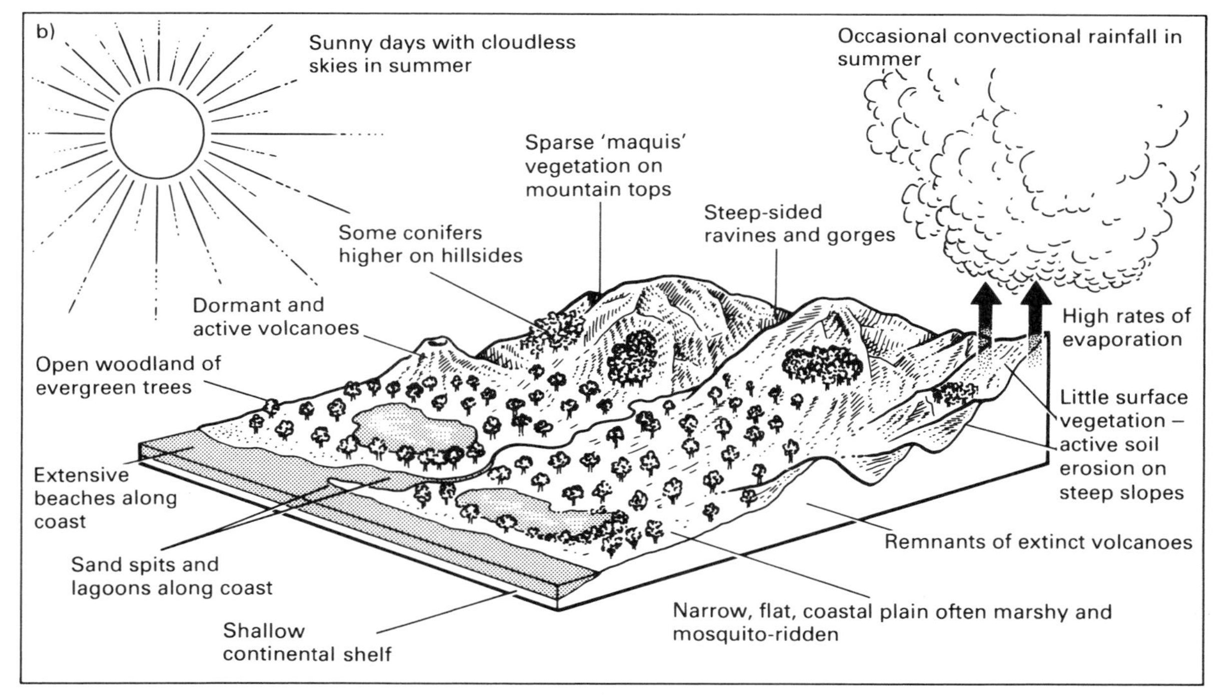

3.7b Summary block diagram of Mediterranean landscape

Zone 6: temperate grasslands and forests

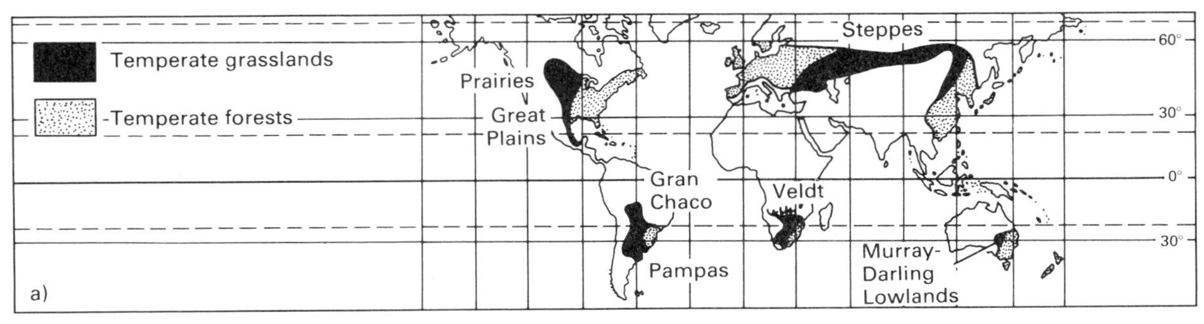

3.8a Distribution of temperate grasslands and forests

Climate

1. Temperature
   a) Very large range (> 25°C) in grassland areas of continental interiors.
   b) Smaller range in coastal areas due to moderating influence of sea.
   c) Cold winters (< 0°C) with snow, warm summers (> 18°C).
2. Rainfall
   a) Can rise to 700 mm in wet coastal areas but decreases inland to 300 mm in places.
   b) High rates of evaporation inland in summer.

Vegetation

1. Vegetation varies with rainfall from dense deciduous forest in wettest areas, through a zone with longer grasses with some shrubs and trees, to areas of low rainfall with short, tufted and wiry grasses.
2. Temperate grasslands are also known as steppe or prairie and contain a great variety of grasses, legumes, e.g. vetch and clover and flora, e.g. daisies and anemones.
3. Temperate forests consist largely of deciduous trees, e.g. oak, beech, maple, hickory, which rarely occur in stands but more commonly as mixed woodland.

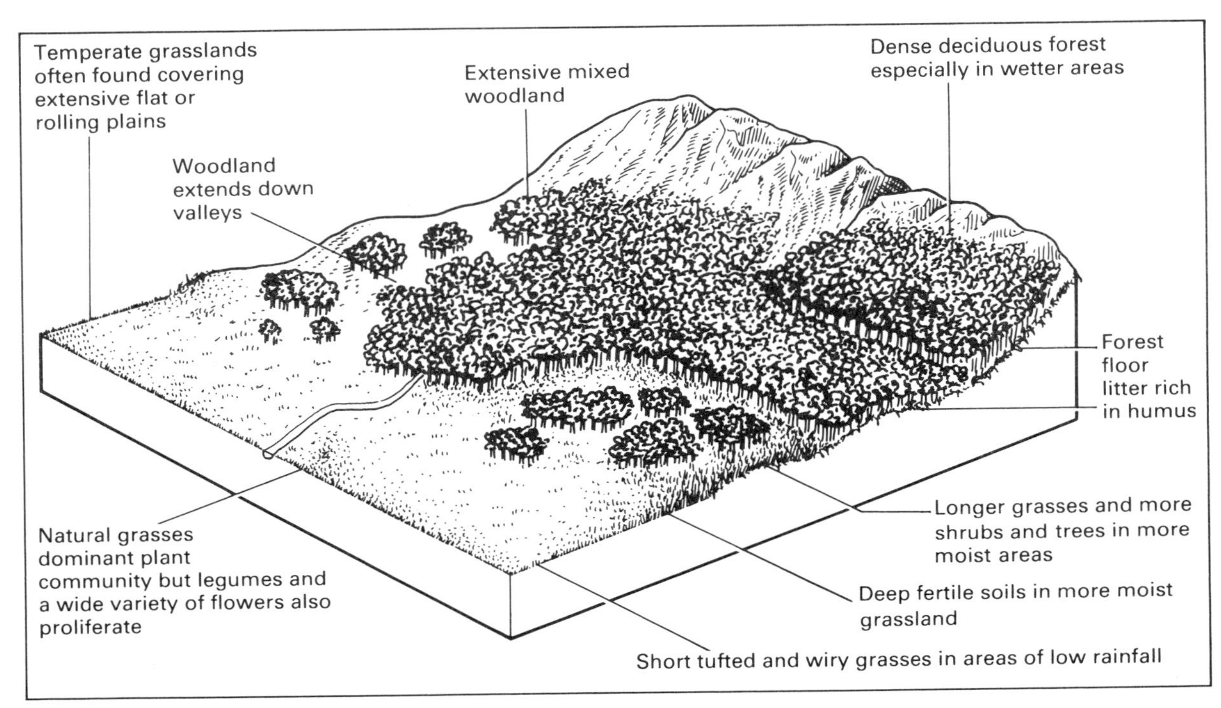

3.8b Summary block diagram of temperate grasslands landscape

Zone 7: coniferous forests (taiga)

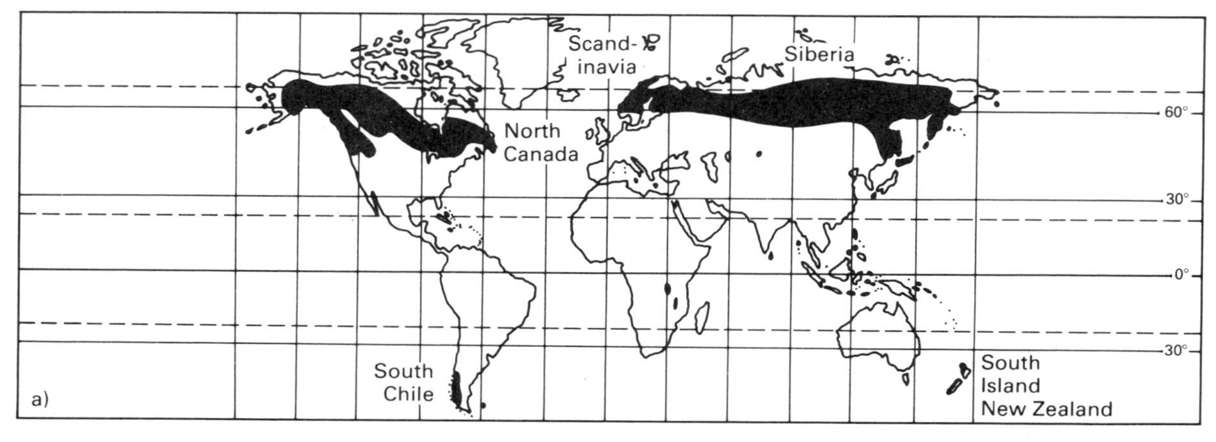

3.9a Distribution of coniferous forest (taiga)

Climate

1. Temperature
   a) Large range (> 20°C) climate of extremes.
   b) Long cold winters (7–8 months), ground frozen and snow-covered.
   c) Summers short (three to five months) but warm (15°C in continental interiors).
2. Rainfall
   a) Varies with distance from sea, falls as snow in winter.
   b) Convectional thunderstorms bring some rainfall to interiors in summer.

Vegetation

1. Coniferous (cone-bearing) trees, e.g. pines, spruces and firs predominate. Larch is only main exception.
2. These evergreen, softwood trees tend to be found in stands of the same variety.
3. Trees are well adapted to climate — they are slow-growing and evergreen, have needle-shaped leaves to reduce transpiration and resist cold, protect seed by means of cones.
4. Little undergrowth tends to be found, needles slowly decompose.

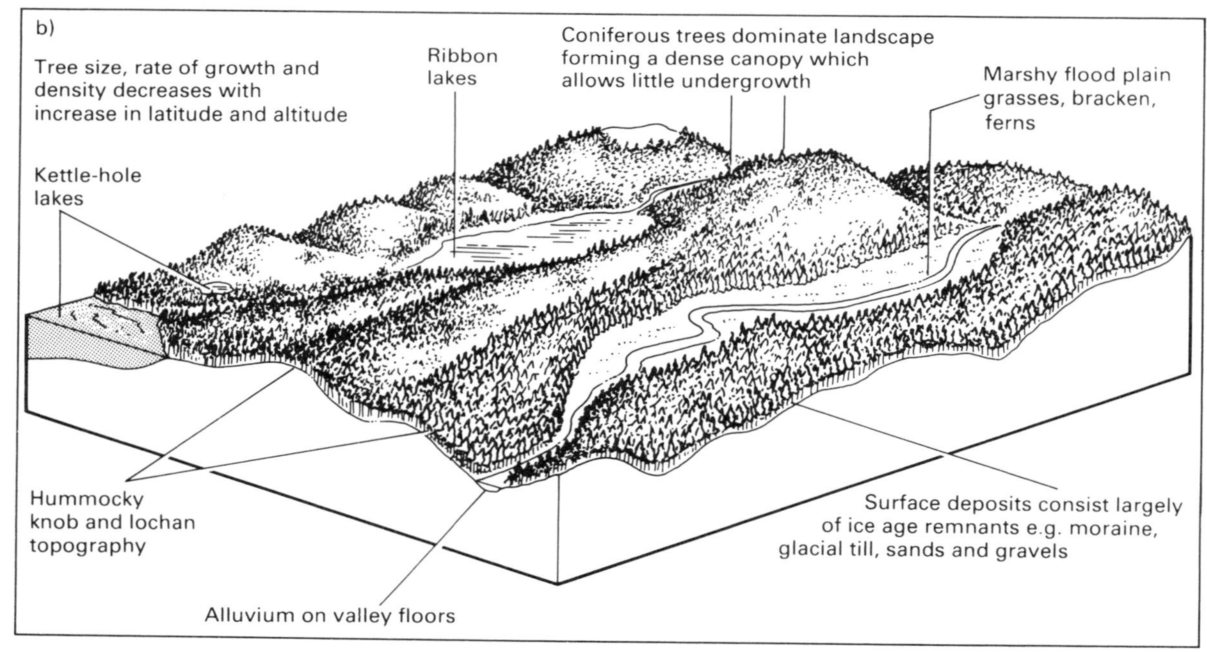

3.9b Summary block diagram of coniferous forest landscape

Zone 8: tundra

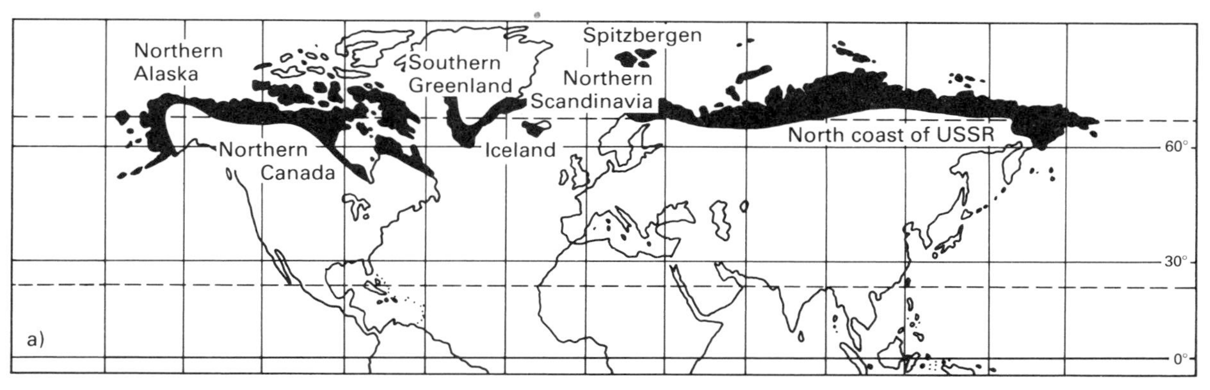

3.10a Distribution of tundra

Climate

1. Temperature
   a) Very large range (> 20°C), extreme climate conditions.
   b) Long, cold, snowy winters (eight months often below freezing), sun never rises in mid-winter, twenty-four hours of darkness.
   c) Short summers (six to twelve weeks) when temperatures rise above 0°C, 24 hours of daylight in mid-summer.
2. Rainfall
   a) Total less than 250 mm — tundra is 'cold desert'.
   b) Most precipitation falls in winter as snow, often in blizzard conditions.

Vegetation

1. All plants require to be able to complete growth cycle in short summer months and to be able to withstand very low winter temperatures.
2. Due to underlying permafrost and thin active layer, plants require shallow roots.
3. Plants tend to be of low and 'ground-hugging' types, e.g. mosses, lichens, saxifrage, heathers. In more sheltered locations bushes, such as bilberry and cranberry and dwarf trees, e.g. birch, willow, ash, alder.
4. The summits of high mountains have similar types of vegetation to the tundra.

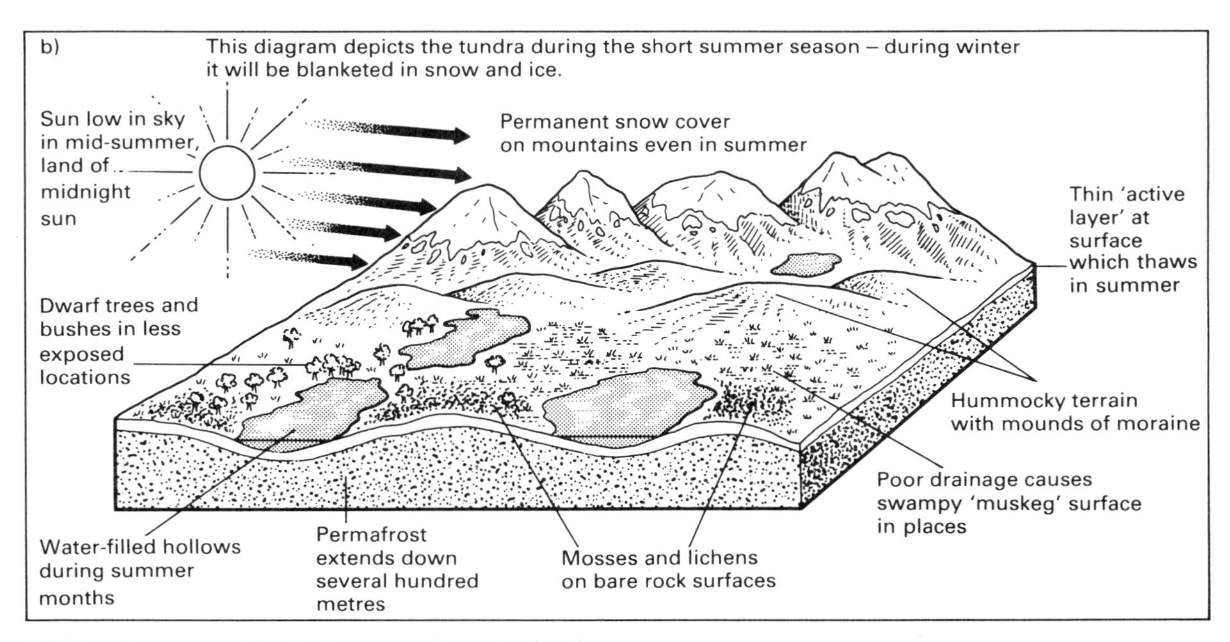

3.10b Summary block diagram of tundra landscape

3.11 Tundra landscape, Iceland

Identifying bioclimatic zones from climate statistics

A set of temperature and rainfall statistics for one particular climate station provides some very strong clues as to which bioclimatic zone it is located within and even to its likely situation in that zone. Provided a systematic approach is taken, such as the one which follows, identification of the bioclimatic zone should be possible without too much difficulty. The checklist below deals with temperature figures at first, in suggesting a possible zone and confirms, or contradicts, this interpretation by later reference to rainfall statistics which also help to pinpoint a more precise location.

Task	Reasoning	Suggested location
1. Temperatures a) Find period of highest temperatures	if highest temperatures in June, July and August if highest temperatures in December, January and February	northern hemisphere southern hemisphere
b) Note maximum and minimum temperatures	if maximum temperature ≥ 28°C if minimum temperature > 15°C[2] if minimum temperature < 15°C if temperatures rarely rise above 0°C	tropical latitudes temperate latitudes temperate latitudes polar latitudes
c) Calculate temperature range	large temperature range (> 25°C) normally experienced a considerable distance from the sea small temperature ranges tend to be found closer to the sea very small temperature range and high (25–30°C) max + min temperatures	continental interior coastal tropical rain forest
2. Rainfall a) Total up annual rainfall	if low total annual rainfall (< 250 mm) if no seasonal pattern but high all year	hot desert or tundra tropical rain forest or temperate forest, grassland
b) Study seasonal distribution pattern of rainfall	if marked summer drought/winter maximum if marked summer wet season/winter dry season if summer maximum this could be due to convectional rainfall	Mediterranean, west coast of continents only savanna or monsoon continental interior

1. In order to allow comparison temperature statistics are normally reduced to sea level.
2. Hot desert locations can be an exception to this general rule.

3.12 Checklist for identifying bioclimatic zones from climate statistics

5. **With reference to Figure 3.4b), account for the apparent zonation of vegetation within the tropical grasslands (savannas) of West Africa.**

6. **Study Fig. 3.5b. Describe the different types of physical landscape found within the hot deserts and explain the reasons for the differences.**

7. **With reference to pressure systems and winds, describe and explain the pattern of rainfall experienced in the Indian sub-continent throughout the year (see Zone 4).**

8. **Compare and contrast the climatic conditions which favour the growth of trees in tropical rainforests and coniferous forests.**

9. **Why are dwarf trees and bushes and 'ground-hugging' plants practically the only types of vegetation to be found in the tundra?**

10. **Study the climate figures below and, using the checklist (Fig. 3.12), identify the bioclimatic zone within which each climate station is located and describe its likely vegetation.**

Station A	J	F	M	A	M	J	J	A	S	O	N	D
Temperature °C	−25	−25	−22	−12	−1	7	14	11	5	−5	−17	−22
Rainfall mm	15	10	15	20	15	20	30	50	25	30	20	15

Station B	J	F	M	A	M	J	J	A	S	O	N	D
Temperature °C	26.1	26.7	27.2	27.2	27.2	27.2	27.2	27.2	27.2	26.7	26.7	26.7
Rainfall mm	252	173	192	198	188	173	173	183	194	206	254	257

Station C	J	F	M	A	M	J	J	A	S	O	N	D
Temperature °C	−15	−11	−5	5	11	14	16	15	10	5	−4	−10
Rainfall mm	23	15	20	23	48	29	84	58	33	18	18	20

4

Soils

Formation/development/profiles

Throughout the world, food supply is dependent on the soil. Although superficially some soils look alike, the principal constituents of soil are present in varying proportions in different places. Even on a very local scale, such as a single farm, there may be wide variations in soil type and fertility and on a world scale it is possible to identify more fundamental differences between soils, such as the fertile **czernozems** of the temperate grasslands and the acid **podzols** of the Taiga.

To some extent, this variation in soils is due to differences in their composition, **solid mineral particles** (for example, weathered rock fragments), **humus** (from the decay of plants), **dead** and **living organisms**, **air** and **water**; and in turn the variations in these soil **inputs** are the result of the interplay of regional differences in soil-forming factors. These factors were identified by the American soil scientist, H Jenny, in the following equation:

$$[S = f(C,G,V,R)t]$$

where S = Soil type, C = Climate, G = Geology or underlying rock, V = vegetation, R = Relief, t = time.

The main usefulness of this formula is in allowing us to identify the main factors which influence soil formation. Clearly, in any specific location the relative importance of any single input is likely to vary, but it is the relationship between these inputs which is reflected in the character of the soil.

The soil as a system

In understanding soil types, it is helpful to consider the soil as a **system**, the form of which is dependent upon three processes: **inputs**, **outputs** and **internal transfer**. This is summarised in Fig. 4.1

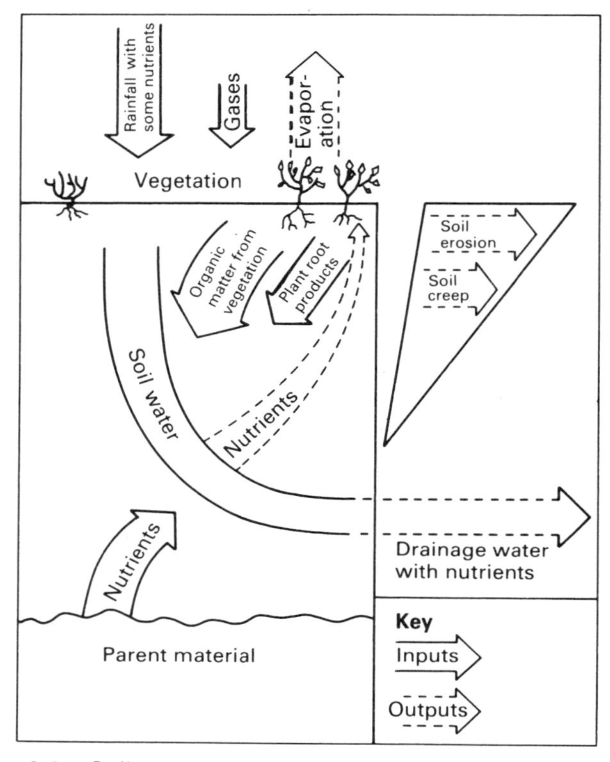

4.1 Soils as a system

Soil profiles

As a result of the internal processes described above, soils tend to develop a series of distinct horizontal layers or **horizons**. These layers (Fig. 4.2) are initially identifiable by variations in

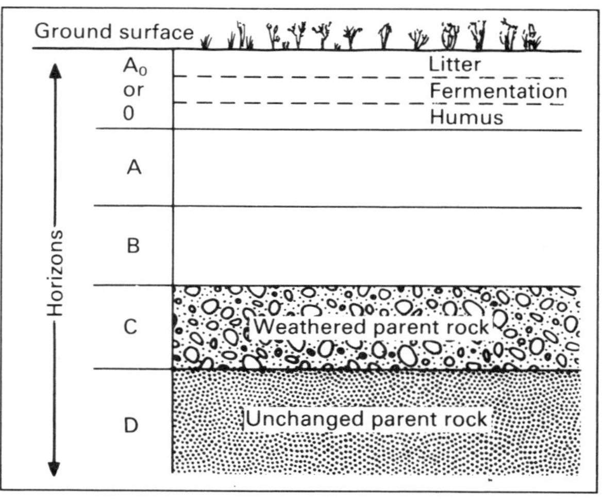

4.2 Basic soil profile

colour and texture, but are also different in their mineral composition and humus content. They are formed as a result of **leaching** or the downward movement of mineral salts in solution, and also as a result of organic processes within the soil.

In the layers closest to the surface, **humus** — organic material derived mostly from vegetation and dead organisms — is gradually broken down by chemical decay and the activity of micro-organisms in the soil. Fig. 4.2 shows that within the surface layer, or Ao horizon, it is possible to identify three sub-layers which represent different stages in the decomposition of the organic matter: **litter** (top layer showing little decomposition); **fermentation** (middle layer which shows signs of decay); and **humus**, the lowest layer where chemical decay is complete and the organic material has become a dark-brown gelatinous substance.

Below these active organic layers, the top, or A horizon is the soil proper, consisting of a mixture of humus and mineral particles. This is followed by the coarser textured B horizon, or **subsoil** which in turn is underlain by the C horizon, usually consisting mainly of weathered rock fragments overlying the solid parent rock, or D horizon.

By using the characteristics found in different soil profiles, soil scientists have been able to develop systems of classification to allow different types of soil to be grouped together.

1. Identify the main factors influencing soil formation, and explain how soil profiles develop.

Classifications: zonal/azonal/intrazonal

Zonal soils

Climate and vegetation are obviously two major influences on soil development and in much the same way that it is possible to identify world zones of natural vegetation (Fig. 3.1, p. 20), there are areas where soils show common characteristics (Fig. 4.3). Although there are clear similarities between these two maps, some scientists have argued that this classification overemphasises the influence of climate and vegetation on soil development and takes insufficient account of local factors such as rock type, drainage and micro-climates. Nonetheless, the concept of zonal soils remains a useful method of describing soil distributions, providing it is borne in mind that they can only reflect very broad climatic and vegetational controls and may conceal regional variations.

Tundra soils (Fig. 4.4)

These occur in areas of tundra vegetation (Fig. 3.10a, p. 29), where the sub-soil remains frozen all year. During the brief periods of summer, the ground surface thaws but free drainage is impeded by the permafrost layer, resulting in waterlogging (or **gleying**). Bacterial action is extremely limited due to the cold temperatures and also to the lack of oxygen in the waterlogged soil; these factors, together with the very limited vegetation of the tundra, make humus formation therefore very slow. The alternating periods of freezing — which results in expansion of the soil, and thawing — which produces contractions, causes considerable

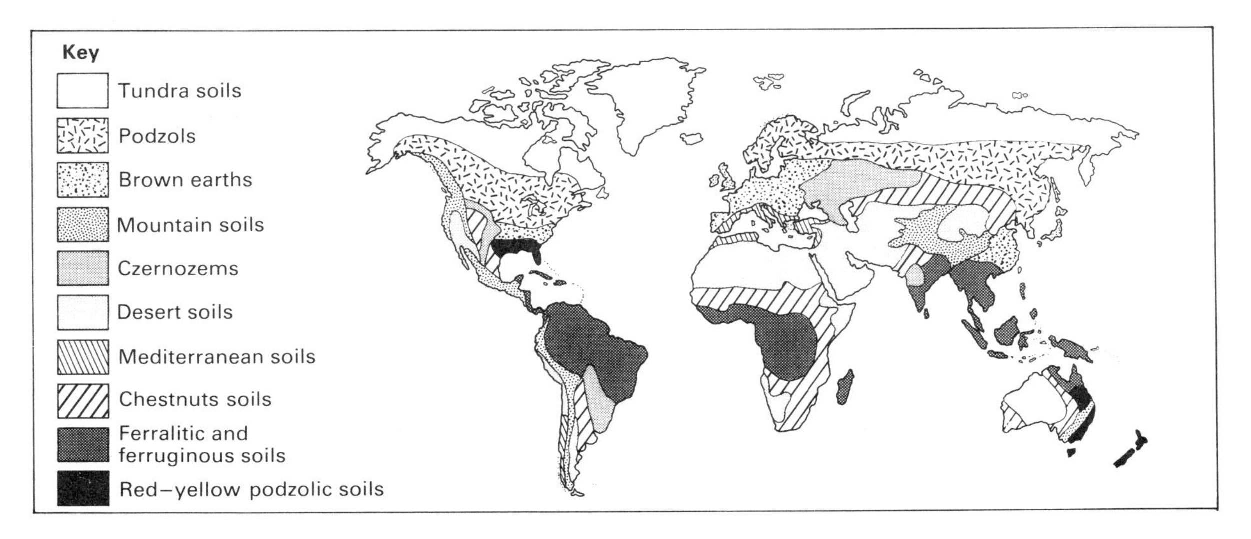

4.3 World soil map

disturbance and mixing within the soil structure and prevents the development of clearly defined horizons. Although weathering of the parent rock is fairly slow in these conditions, tundra soils nevertheless contain numerous angular frost-shattered rock fragments within the blue-grey peaty clays which characterise tundra soils.

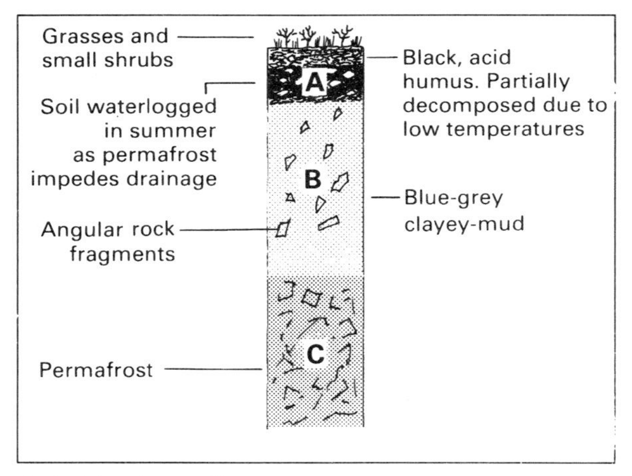

4.4 Tundra soil

Podzols (Fig. 4.5)

Podzols are found in a broad latitudinal belt across the northern hemisphere and are particularly associated with the belt of taiga or coniferous forest natural vegetation (Fig. 3.9a, p. 28). The extensive areas of pine trees have a poor nutrient cycle: their uptake of mineral salts from the soil is restricted and as a result the fall of tree cones and needles is deficient in bases creating an acid or **mor** humus. Winters are very cold and long and decomposition of debris in the Ao horizon is very slow with little change taking place over many months. Although precipitation is not excessive, the process of podzolisation begins when the spring melt releases water previously stored as snow and ice creating strong **leaching** of iron and aluminium oxides from the A horizon and leaving behind a high silica residue. The absence of earthworms due to the cold climate restricts mixing of the horizons and results in particularly well-defined layers. These are accentuated by variations in colouring, with the upper horizons below the humus much lighter due to the removal of minerals. The concentration of the iron and aluminium oxides in the B horizon may produce a 'cementing' effect enough to create a **hardpan** which can impede drainage through the soil and create waterlogging in the upper layers.

Grey-brown forest soils (Fig. 4.6)

These soils are generally located further south than true podzols and where higher temperatures and a longer growing season encourage the growth of broad-leaved deciduous trees (Fig. 3.8a, p. 27). The nutrient cycle is very active, with annual leaf-fall returning bases to the soil, the milder climatic conditions encouraging more rapid decomposition, and the production of a more alkaline or **mull** humus. There is much greater mixing of debris into the soil and between layers by earthworms, insects and rodents. Tree roots may go very deep, even into the parent rock, to draw up minerals. Leaching still takes place as precipitation exceeds evaporation, but is not usually excessive enough to remove all mineral content and humus from the upper layers. Consequently colouring tends to gradually become paler with greater depth.

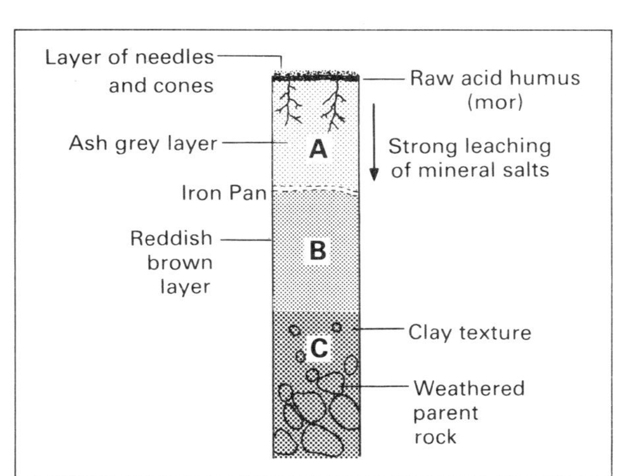

4.5 Podzol soil

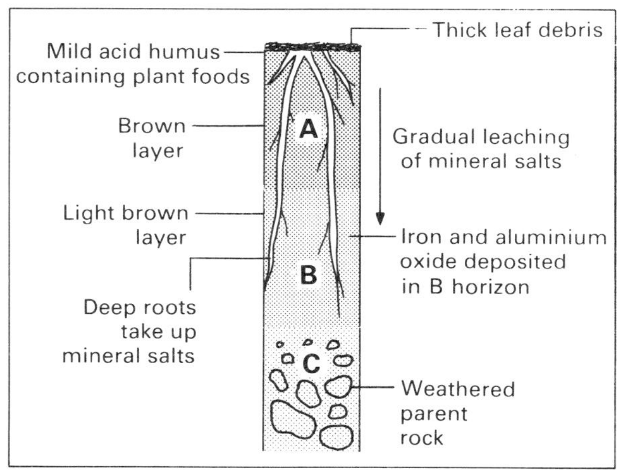

4.6 Grey-brown forest soil

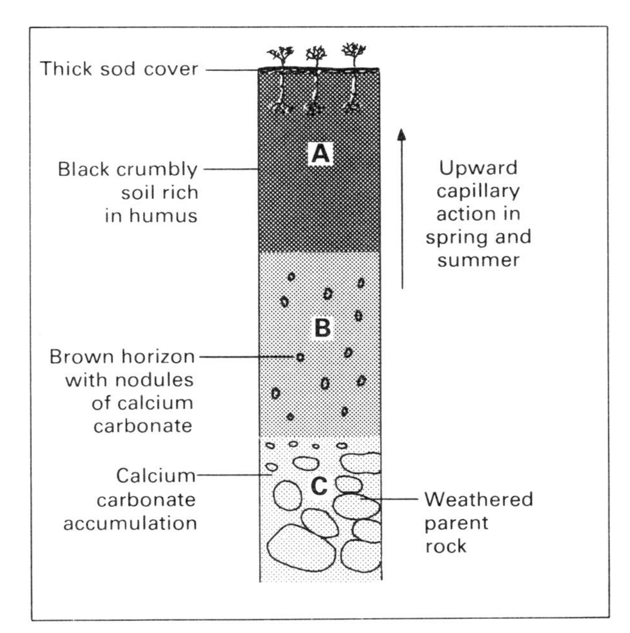

4.7 Czernozem soil

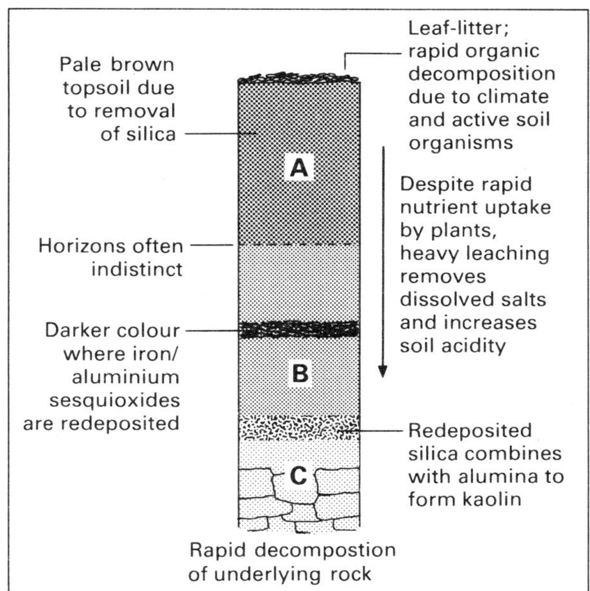

4.8 Tropical red-brown soil

Czernozems (Fig. 4.7)

Sometimes referred to as 'black earths', czernozem soils are associated with temperate grassland areas (Fig. 3.8a, p. 27) which experience drier and milder conditions than the forest areas further north. Even so, winters are often extremely cold, particularly in continental interior areas which may experience very high snowfalls. During the spring melt, water percolates down through the soil, leaching salts downwards, but during the summer much drier and warmer weather encourages the nutrients to move back up through the soil by the process of **capillary rise**: thus minerals are moved up into the plant rooting zone at the time of maximum plant growth. This upward movement also results in the concentration of calcium carbonate nodules in the middle and lower parts of the soil as lime-rich solutions are evaporated. The upper horizons are often very dark in colour and tend to be loose and crumbly, and this, coupled with high soil fertility, due to the productive nutrient cycle and good drainage, contributes to the high agricultural value of czernozem soils, which tend to be used principally for cereal cultivation in areas such as the Steppes of the USSR and the North American Prairies.

Tropical red-brown soils (Fig. 4.8)

Sometimes called **latosols**, these soils are found in association with tropical rain forest vegetation (Fig. 3.3a, p. 22). Despite the luxuriant forest vegetation of these areas, the impression of fertility is illusory and is due largely to the rapid recycling of nutrients from leaf litter to humus in the surface soil. Removal of the forest vegetation exposes the soil to erosion due to alternating periods of hot sun and heavy rainfall, under which conditions vegetation may take many years to regenerate.

Due to the constant high temperatures, bacterial activity is high. The A horizon is usually pale-brown in colour after the removal of soluble silica by leaching due to the heavy rainfall. The climate also causes very rapid chemical weathering, leaving reddish deposits of iron and aluminium **sesquioxides** in the middle-layers of the soil. Occasionally, due to intense precipitation of the iron minerals, these may become concentrated into a hard crust or **laterite** which may occur either at the surface or in the subsoil.

Although the grouping of world soils into **zonal** types linked with climatic and vegetation characteristics is a convenient system of classification, it has been criticised for being over-simplistic and for paying insufficient regard to local factors. For example, within any of the bio-climatic regions there will obviously be considerable variations in underlying rock type, drainage patterns and relief, all of which have considerable influence on the development of soils. In such cases, **intrazonal** soil types may develop, and, as the name suggests are not confined to any one of the zones, but may occur anywhere in the world where particular localised conditions are more important than bio-climatic factors. Examples would include **gley** soils which are associated with waterlogged conditions, and the alkaline **rendzina** soils found in temperate areas with underlying limestone which counteracts the natural tendency to podsolisation.

All of these soil types have developed their characteristic profiles and can be recognised by their distinctive horizons. **Azonal soils**, however, have usually been formed relatively recently and so have been little affected by the usual soil-forming processes such as leaching, and are not associated with particular bio-climatic regions. These soils include the alluvial deposits on river flood plains, volcanic soils and glacial moraines.

2. Explain what is meant by a zonal soil.

3. Czernozems and grey-brown forest soils are examples of zonal soils. For each, describe and explain the effects of climate and natural vegetation on the development of the soil profile.

4. Analyse the limitations of podzols and tropical red earth soils for agricultural development.

5. What do you understand by the terms 'intrazonal' and 'azonal' soils? Describe the natural conditions under which such soils develop.

Soil erosion

Soil erosion takes place principally when land is exposed to the action of **wind** and **rain**. With a lack of vegetation cover and in the absence of rooted plants, soil particles are easily loosened and washed away during heavy rainstorms or blown away in strong winds.

Types of soil erosion

1. Wind erosion takes place principally in arid regions or areas of marginal climates such as the **Sahel**, which may experience periods of drought allowing soils to dry out. Where vegetation cover has been removed, soils are liable to be reduced to dust and blown away. The most famous example of soil erosion resulting from wind erosion took place in the USA during the 1930s. As monocultural wheat farming spread across the Great Plains about the time of the First World War, the area under cultivation increased dramatically, as did the use of machinery. In the State of Kansas alone, wheat hectarage increased from around two million ha in 1910 to almost five million ha in 1919. During the late 1920s and early 1930s a series of hot, dry years caused crop failures and dried up the soil, making it susceptible to wind erosion. The resulting so-called **dust-bowl** created black clouds which stretched from Canada to Texas, and from Montana to Ohio.

'*. . . a four day storm in May 1934 . . . transported some 300 million tons of dirt 1500 miles, darkened New York, Baltimore and Washington for five hours and dropped dust not only on the President's desk in the White House, but also on the decks of ships some 300 miles out in the Atlantic.*'
(Coffey, M. 1978)

2. Sheet erosion is often difficult to detect in early stages because it results in the removal of a uniform depth of soil across large areas (Fig. 4.9). The only evidence that erosion is taking place is the gradual exposure of tree roots and fencing stakes. It has been estimated that the loss of only 1.5 cm of topsoil in an average field results in a soil loss of about 190 tonnes per hectare.

3. Gully erosion takes place on land which is sloping (Fig. 4.9). Surface water run-off washes away soil and creates small channels or **rills** in natural depressions. Often these rills enlarge into deep channels or **gullies** which cut deep into the land surface. In India, it is estimated that gully erosion results in loss of about 8000 ha of cultivable land each year.

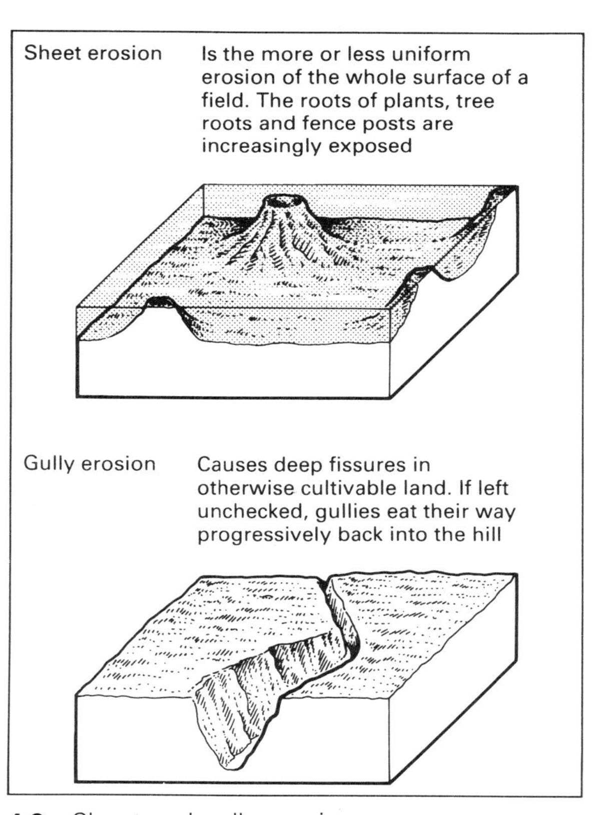

4.9 Sheet and gully erosion

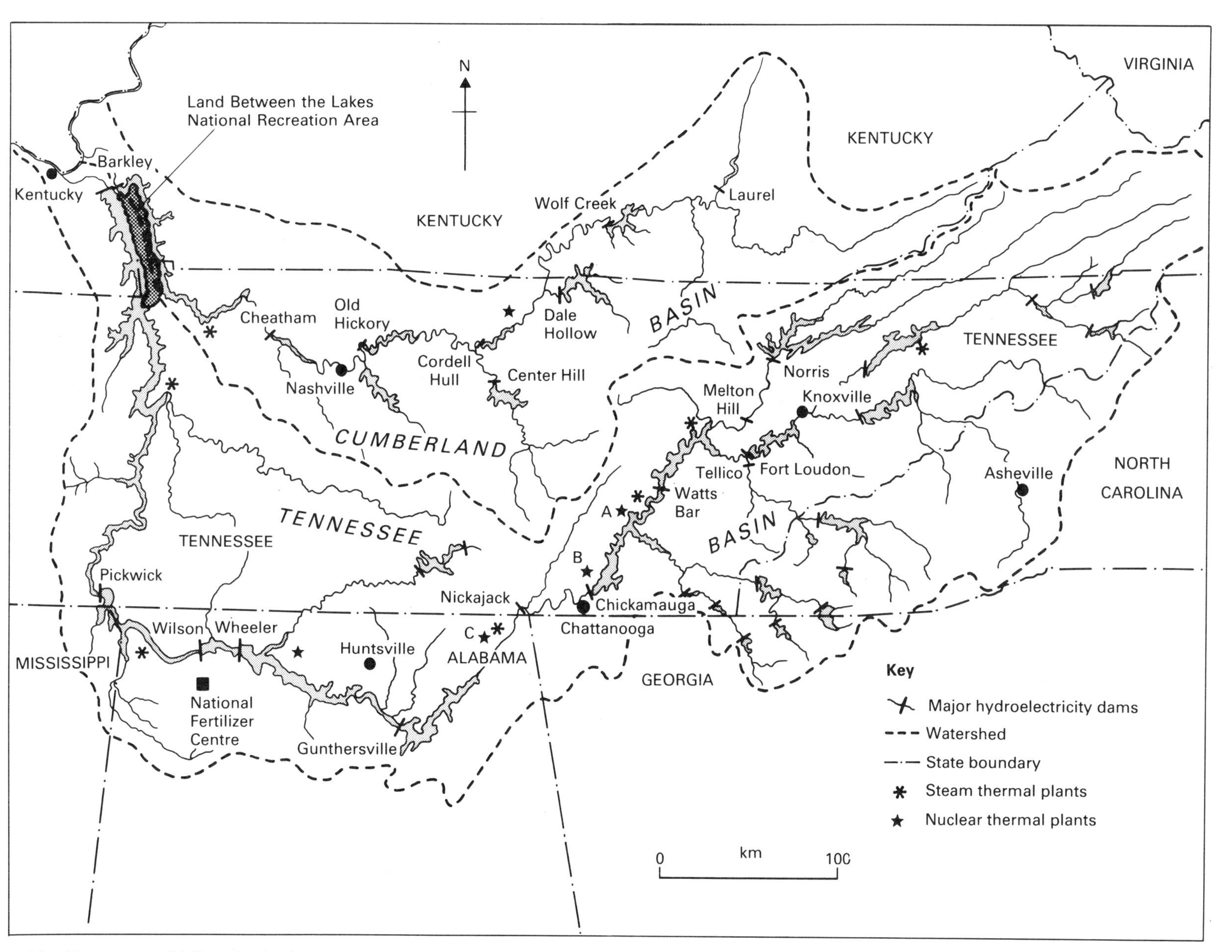

4.10 Tennessee Valley Authority

Causes of soil erosion

Although climatic factors such as high winds, drought and heavy rainfall may be the catalysts in soil erosion, the underlying causes owe much more to human interference and in particular to land being farmed beyond its capability. Perhaps the most famous example of an area which suffered severe soil erosion and has been successful in undertaking a programme of conservation is the area covered by the Tennessee Valley Authority in the south of the USA (Fig. 4.10).

Tennessee Valley Authority: case study

The Tennessee River is formed by a large number of tributary streams which rise in Virginia's Blue Ridge Mountains before flowing into the main valley trough where they merge to become the Tennessee proper. The river flows in a south-westerly direction as far as Chattanooga where it turns west and cuts through the southern edge of the Appalachian Plateau, and then flows north to join the Ohio River, just before its confluence with the Mississippi.

During the depression of the 1930s, the Tennessee Valley represented rural America's most pressing problems. To the area north-east of Chattanooga, the inhabitants were mainly poor farmers living in considerable poverty. Their land plots were too small to provide an adequate living and the soils too infertile and shallow for productive agriculture. Ignorance of even the most elementary soil conservation practises had resulted in widespread soil erosion (Fig. 4.12a). 'Hungry crops' such as maize and tobacco were grown year after year to increase income, but rows of crops were planted on steep slopes and infertile plots left bare of vegetation. Farm incomes fell dramatically as crop prices slumped, and the once-forested hillsides, now cleared by the valley's poor 'hillbilly' farmers, were the subject of massive soil erosion. As well as affecting agricultural productivity in the upstream areas which lost vast quantities of soil, the movement downstream of river sediments caused the water flow to be unpredictable, presenting an acute flood danger to low-lying farms and urban areas, as well as making the river almost useless for navigation. An additional problem caused by the flooding was the creation of many stagnant pools which provided ideal breeding grounds for malarial mosquitoes, and in 1933 it was estimated that over half of the local population suffered from the disease.

In 1933 President Roosevelt created the **Tennessee Valley Authority** (TVA), a federal body to co-ordinate work between the seven states which share the 100 000 km^2 river basin. The new Authority had several functions:

— Control of soil erosion
— Reclamation of eroded farmland and valley sides
— Promotion of better farming methods
— Construction of dams to control the river flow
— Generation and sale of hydro-electricity
— Navigational improvements

From these six principal aims developed several linkages and multiplier effects as a result of the investment by the TVA in the area (Fig. 4.13). The Norris Dam, the first of over thirty dams across the valley, was already under construction before the end of 1933 and in order to reduce soil erosion many thousands of tree seedlings were planted as part of a massive **reforestation** programme on the upper valley slopes (Fig. 4.12b). Today, well in excess of half of the entire area covered by the TVA is forested. Other farming improvements, such as the widespread use of contour ploughing, controlled grazing and inter-cropping, were achieved by the establishment of education units for local farmers in association with agricultural colleges, and in 1934 a phosphate plant was opened at Muscle Shoals to produce fertilizers. This developed into the National Fertilizer Development Centre, which has continued to assist agricultural innovation in the area. The expansion of electricity production in the area attracted several new industries, which provided alternative employment to agriculture, and many farmers moved into the expanding towns of the lower Valley, allowing the reorganisation of land-holdings into larger, more economically viable units. As further dams and reservoirs were constructed and flood control became effective, waterfront sites were developed for housing and industry. Companies which were established near to the river were able to take advantage of the improved navigational facilities which had created a three metre channel from Knoxville to the Ohio River: between 1933 and 1970 cargo movements on the Tennessee increased from less than one million tonnes each year to over twenty-five million tonnes. The reservoirs themselves were developed as recreational areas with the provision of park sites and camping facilities which have proved popular with the expanded urban population of the region.

Although the work of the Authority has clearly had a profound effect on the regional development of the Valley over the last fifty years, some observers have criticised the TVA for its pre-occupation with electricity production. By the early 1950s, 80% of farms had access to electricity, compared with a mere 3% in 1933, and the availability of cheap power had attracted a number of industrial employers to the Valley, particularly those with high power inputs such as the metallurgical industry. So successful was industrial development that demand for power rapidly outstripped the capacity of the five hydro stations, which were supplemented by seven coal-fired stations by 1968 and four nuclear generators by 1974. Some critics of the Authority have argued that this has led to the over-industrialisation of the area and has led to pollution resulting from both the industries themselves, the thermal power stations and also to the vast open cast coal-mines which the Authority have developed to supply the power stations. Against these criticisms must be weighed the achievements of flood control, navigation, reforestation, agricultural improvement, soil conservation and the fact that in 1933 the average family income in the TVA area was only 45% of the US average. In 1980 it was 80% of the national figure in an area where living costs are relatively low.

6. Describe the agents by which, and the conditions under which, soil erosion can be created.
7. The TVA was established as a 'multi-purpose rural management scheme'. Explain what you understand by this statement.
8. Using the text and Fig. 4.12a, identify the main causes of soil erosion in the Tennessee Valley during the 1930s.
9. What soil conservation measures have been encouraged by the TVA? (Fig. 4.12b).
10. Using Fig. 4.13 as a base, explain the achievements of the TVA in promoting rural development.

4.11 Tennessee Valley Authority dam

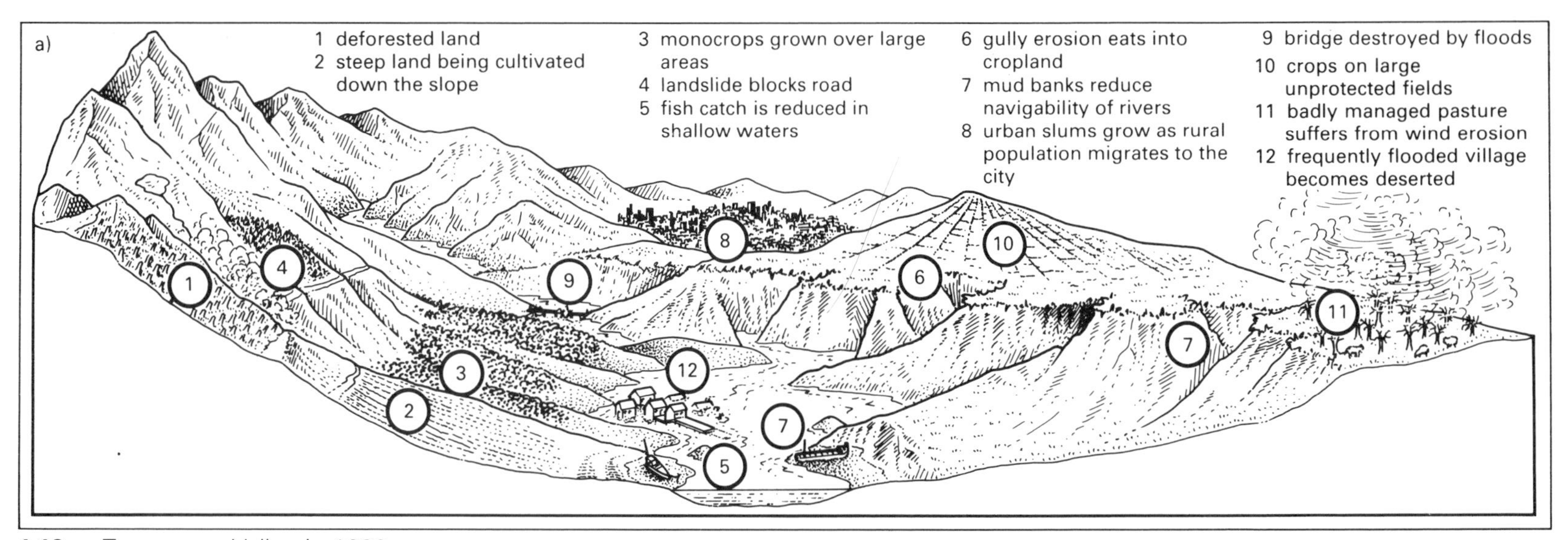

4.12a Tennessee Valley in 1930s

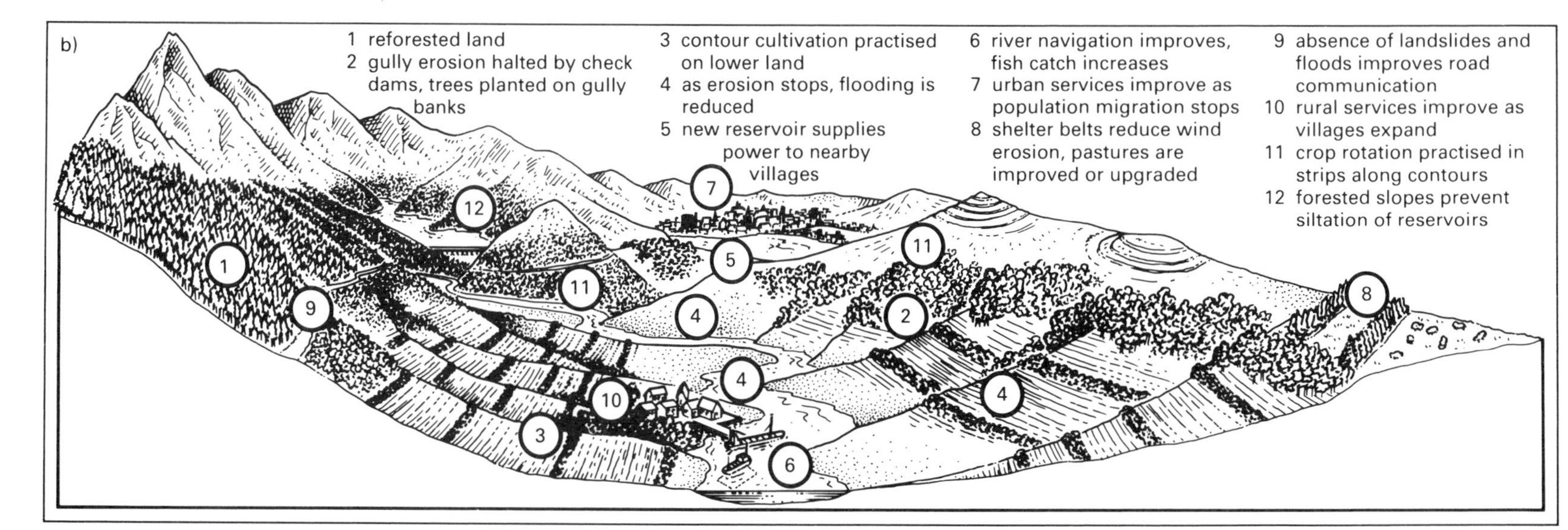

4.12b Work of the Tennessee Valley Authority

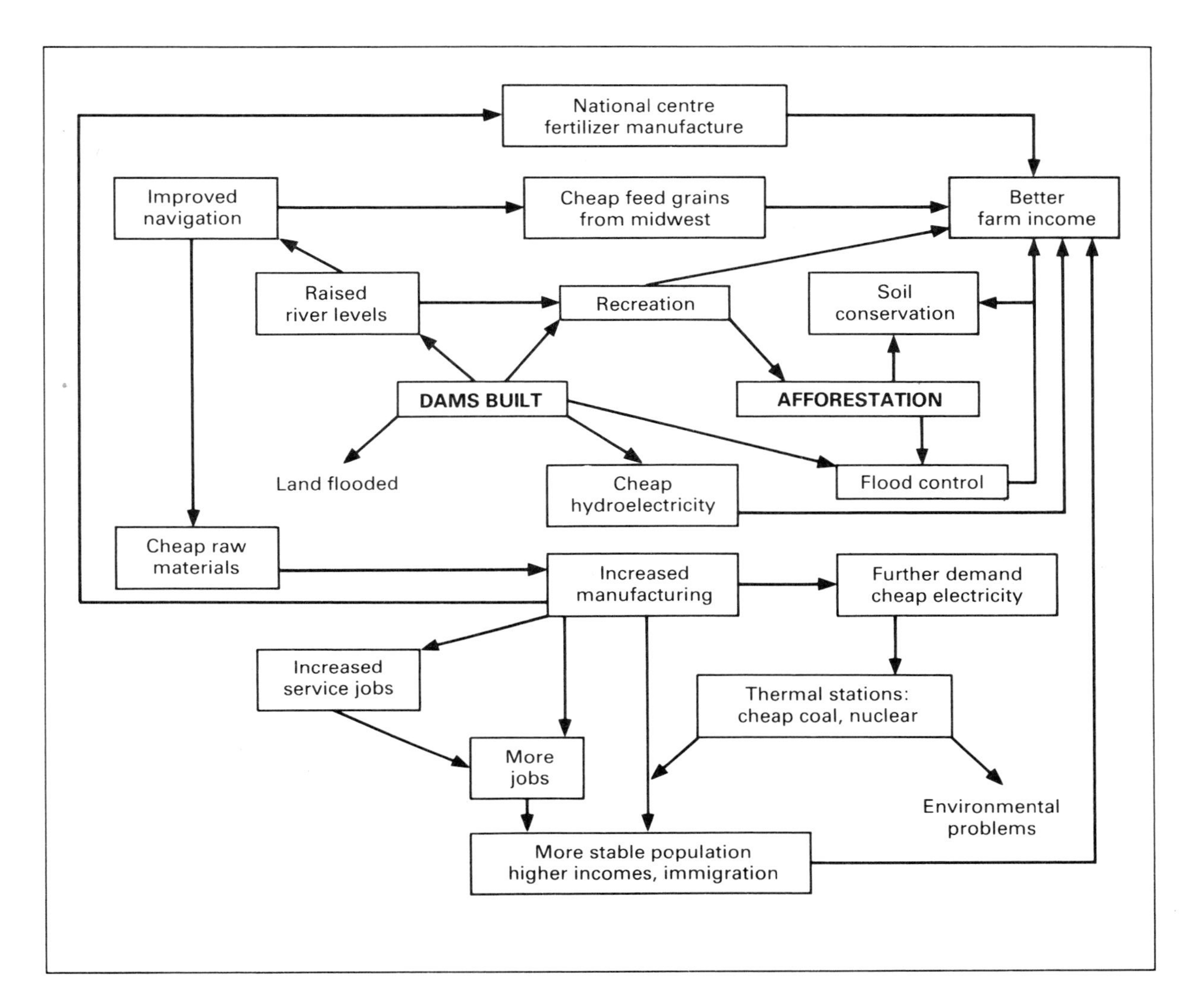

4.13 Linkages and multiplier effects arising from TVA investment

5

Water resources I — the direct use of water

Introduction

As you may remember from the first two chapters of this book, 71% of the Earth's surface area consists of water, of which some 97% is salty and found in the oceans and seas. This leaves only 3% as fresh water, three quarters of which is frozen into the permanent ice-caps, leaving only a quarter (0.75% of the total salt and fresh water available) in our lakes and rivers and underground sources, to satisfy all of our water needs and to circulate within the hydrological cycle (see Fig. 2.8, p. 15). This, the first of two chapters on these water resources, looks at 'direct' human use of water resources, where water itself is actually used. Chapter 10 is concerned with more indirect uses.

Human demands on the world's fresh water supplies have greatly increased through time but have also diversified in terms of types of use. Perhaps the most basic of all demands on fresh water is to meet the requirements of the human metabolism, which consists of 60% water in any case, but which requires on average between two and two and a half litres per day to adequately maintain normal bodily functions. Domestic use also makes huge demands upon fresh water resources, especially in the developed countries. In the USA for example, 454 litres (100 gallons) per day is the average consumption, whereas in Britain it is rather less at 195 litres (forty-three gallons) per day. By far the largest percentage of this water in these countries is used for just three main purposes: flushing toilets, washing and

5.1 Desalination plant Qatar

bathing. Domestic use is therefore one of the major 'abstractive' uses of fresh water, where these resources are actually used up and are lost, at least in the medium term, from the hydrological cycle. The other main abstractive uses are:

— in industry, e.g. in boilers for making steam, in cooling towers
— in the food and drink industry as a raw material, and as a means of waste disposal
— in agriculture, especially for irrigation purposes.

Non-abstractive uses, where water is diverted from its natural course and later returned as surface water, have also contributed to the generally increased demand for fresh water. One major non-abstractive use, which is now prevalent in many lesser developed as well as developed countries, is in the production of hydro-electric power. In many countries, possible sources of fresh water are also used for navigational and recreational purposes.

Interference in the hydrological cycle

In order to cater for the ever-increasing human demands for fresh water, it is necessary to 'interfere' with the hydrological cycle in order to extract our requirements. The cycle has been estimated to have more than half a million cubic kilometres of fresh water flowing within it and it is during two phases of the cycle, runoff and storage, that extraction has proved to be most practicable (see Fig. 2.8, p. 15). Unfortunately, extracting during the runoff phase is much more difficult in some regions of the world than others as runoff (precipitation minus evapotranspiration) is very unevenly distributed across the Earth's surface. In general, the areas of lowest runoff lie in a near-continuous belt which stretches across northern Africa through the Arabian peninsula and on into central Asia. The south-west of North America is also a region of low runoff. At the other extreme, with relatively high runoff, lie areas such as northern South America, the equatorial regions within Africa and much of south-east Asia. It is in these areas of high runoff that many of the world's major rivers are to be found. In contrast, few major rivers, with the possible exception of the Nile in Africa, either traverse or flow within regions of low runoff. In areas of low runoff, extraction of ground-water, during the storage phase, has assumed considerable importance.

Within these phases, water can be extracted at various stages, for example through intervention in surface or immediate sub-surface flow or during natural storage either on the surface or as ground-water. In more recent times, human ingenuity has allowed us to exert some control over runoff through alteration of vegetation cover and also to increase natural storage capacity by the construction of dams, artificial lakes and reservoirs. Other phases of the water cycle have also been the subject of some attention, two of the most notable being efforts at weather modification by '**cloud seeding**' and the recent attempt to tow a huge iceberg containing millions of cubic litres of fresh water to the Middle East from the Antartic. In several countries of the world, especially around the Persian Gulf where several oil-rich states have money available for large capital-intensive projects, desalination plants, where mineral salts are removed from sea-water by an MSF (mutiple storage flash) distillation process, are making an increasing contribution to meeting rapidly rising demands for fresh water (see Fig. 5.1).

Human interference in the water cycle is not something new; it has been going on for thousands of years. It is, however, probably true to say that the scale of this interference has increased significantly through time and that we have become more and more ambitious in suggesting, and at times attempting, larger scale projects.

1. 'The human metabolism . . . requires on average between two and two and a half litres per day to adequately maintain bodily functions'. Under what types of climatic condition is the human metabolism likely to require considerably more than average amounts of fresh water per day? State reasons why in your answer.

2. With 'fresh water' at its centre, and uses round about, draw and annotate a simple diagram to summarise the many human demands upon fresh water in the world today. Subdivide the uses into abstractive and non-abstractive types.

3. Study Fig. 2.8 (p. 15) and go on to explain how the input/output balance is preserved in the hydrological or water cycle.

4. a) Why does human interference in the water cycle take place largely within the runoff and ground-water phases?
   b) Identify any exceptions to this general pattern which have been tried.

Small-scale intervention for domestic water supply and irrigation

In the earliest times, human intervention in the water cycle normally took a very simple form involving extraction from a single point or series of points. Perhaps the classic, and simplest, example of this is the well which acted, and still acts, as the major source of fresh water for millions of people across the world. Small storage tanks or reservoirs which were 'topped up' during periods of excess rainfall fulfilled a similar function as a primary source of fresh water especially in monsoon lands such as India and Sri Lanka. Traditional methods of 'lifting' water for irrigation purposes e.g. the shaduf, sakia and Archimedes screw (Fig. 5.2), also made use of single point sources of extraction. The fact that many of these systems are still in widespread use across the world to this day bears testimony to the simplicity and appropriateness of the technology involved in their use.

Intervention at river basin scale

As Fig. 5.3 shows, the water cycle within river basins is now subject to considerable human intervention for a wide range of different purposes. The construction of dams across the upper course of major rivers and their tributaries has been in widespread use to prevent flooding for centuries now. In a sense, these were the earliest multi-purpose water schemes as they also created storage reservoirs from which water could be extracted for other uses as well. More recently, dams across the upper course of rivers have increasingly been used to generate hydro-electric power and to regulate river flow such that water can be extracted further downstream for domestic, industrial or irrigation use as required (Fig. 5.3).

Perhaps the simplest of sites for irrigation purposes is to be found in the middle and upper courses of river valleys where water can be led off from the water course at a sluice-gate, barrage or dam and directed downslope, due to gravity, along a network of channels or canals. In areas where the force of gravity cannot be made use of, such '**perennial irrigation**' has to make use of power sources such as electricity, diesel or solar energy (see Fig. 5.2) to 'lift' and/or pump the water to a storage point near to the required area. Thereafter, depending upon the type of system which can be afforded, a further network of canals, sprinklers or drip feed pipes deliver the water to the plants.

In the past, people living in the lower parts of river basins often used to make use of what was known as 'basin irrigation', diverting excess water during periods of flooding along inundation canals to the fields. Not surprisingly, there are now very few areas where this is still practised, but in

5.2a Traditional irrigation, Persian wheel (Sakia)

5.2b Modern irrigation, electrically powered pump

5.2c Traditional irrigation (Shaduf)

5.2d Modern irrigation (drip and trickle)

general the level of sophistication of irrigation systems varies greatly in developed and developing areas of the world. In certain low-lying countries, human intervention has even taken place near to the mouths of rivers where barrages have been constructed and fresh-water lakes created within deltas, estuaries or bays. The two best examples are probably to be found in The Netherlands, the Zuider Zee Scheme (Fig. 5.4), and the Rhine Delta Scheme (Fig. 5.5).

As larger and larger proportions of the fresh-water available within river basins have been brought into human use, largely due to technological advances, so the planning of the use of these resources has become an increasingly sophisticated process. One of the earliest examples of a 'whole basin' scheme was begun in 1933 by the Tennessee Valley Authority (TVA) in the USA (see Fig. 4.10, p. 37). Under the TVA scheme (as previously described in chapter 4) a fully integrated water resource development plan was implemented throughout the 100 000 km^2 of the Tennessee River basin, incorporating all aspects of flood control, water supply, hydro-electric power, river navigation and irrigation. Initially, this scheme was planned to control: a) a river regime which frequently produced flood conditions due to excessive convectional rainfall in summer, and b) the acute soil erosion problems which resulted from the periodically high surface runoff and ill-considered farming methods. The other benefits

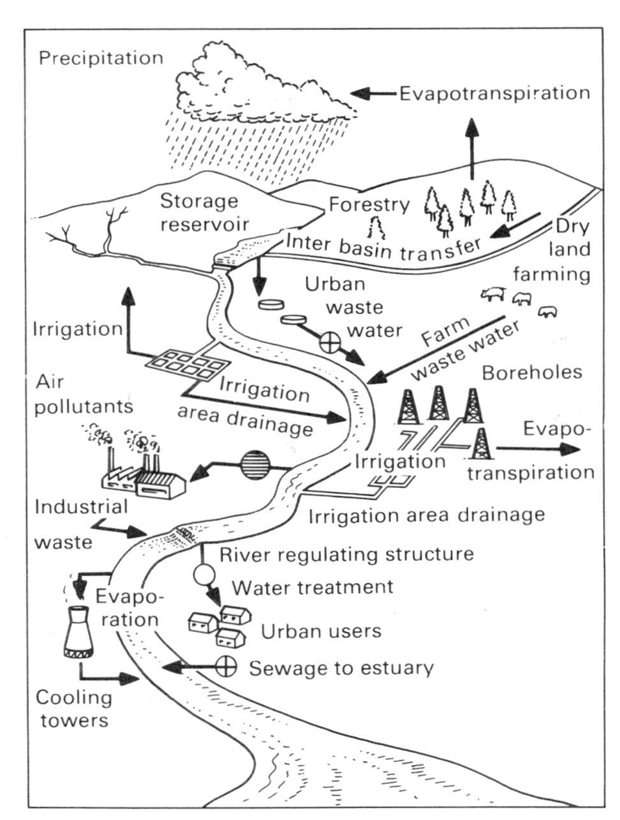

5.3 Effects of human activity on the water cycle within a river basin

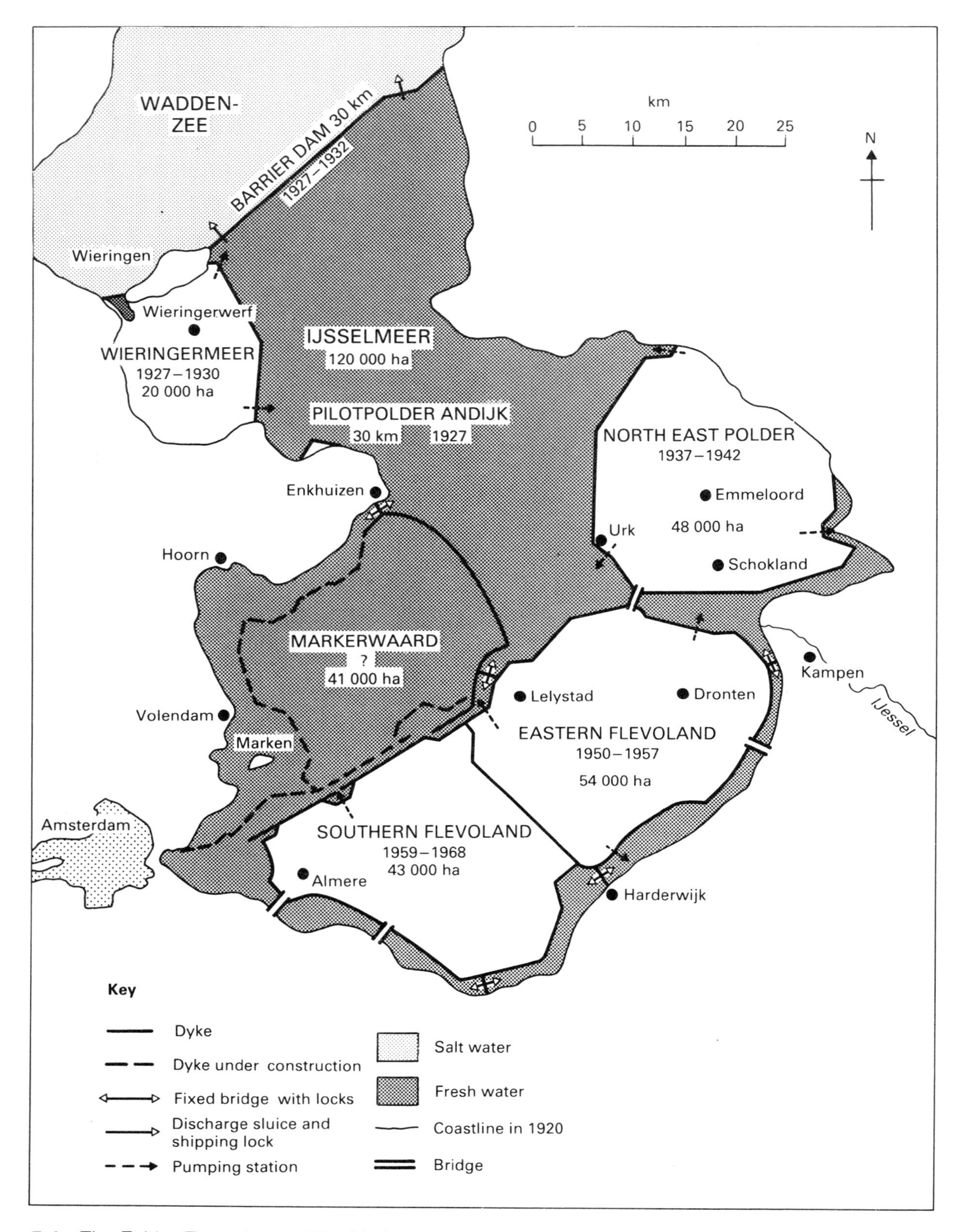

5.4 The Zuider Zee scheme, The Netherlands

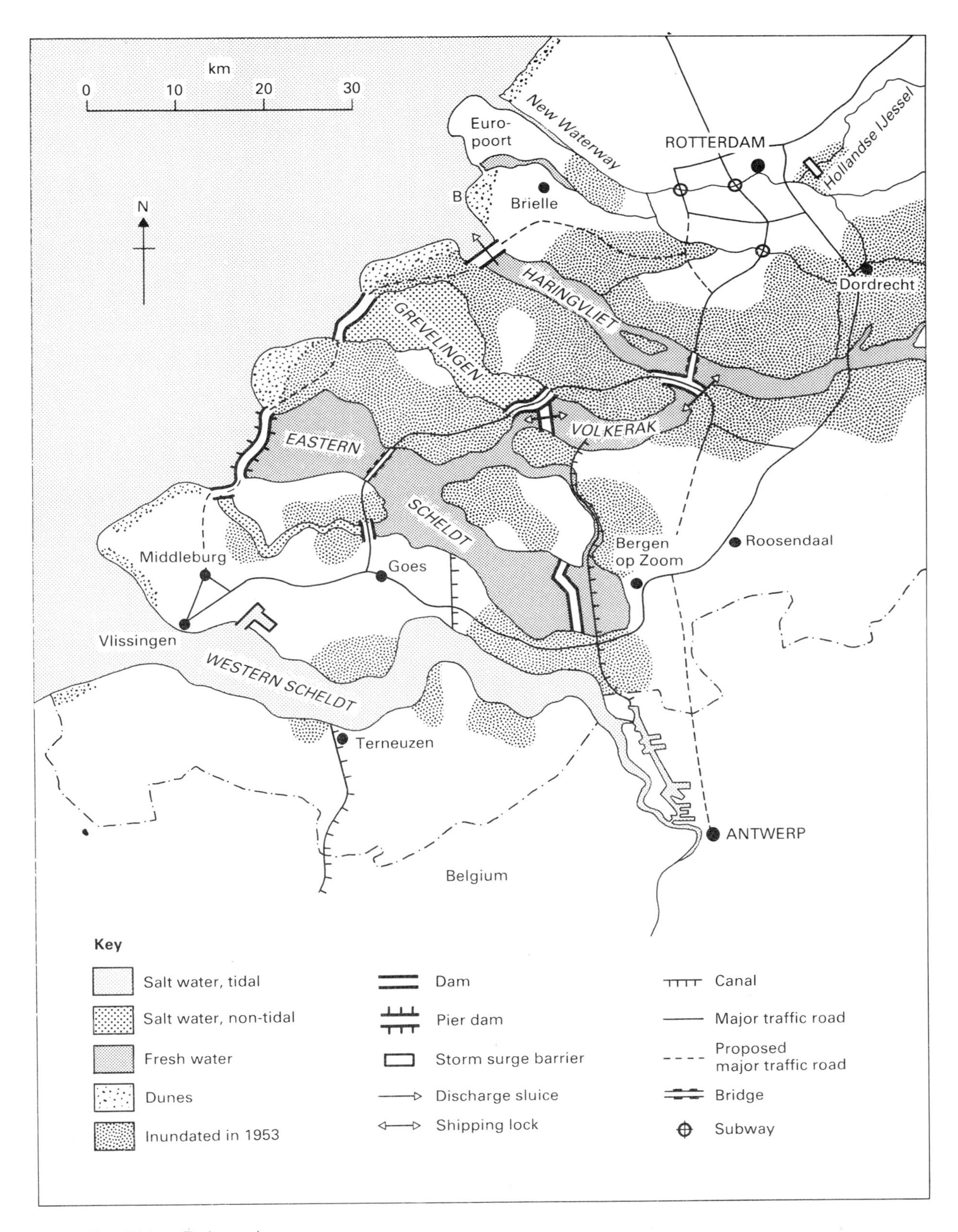

5.5 The Rhine Delta scheme

which have been included within and have accrued from the TVA scheme have been a bonus, but as Fig. 4.10 reveals, the Tennessee River Valley and its major tributary valleys now have a continuous string of dams and lakes and have lost a large area of flat and potentially very valuable valley-floor land.

Large scale multi-purpose water schemes

Few of the multi-purpose water schemes which have been developed since TVA have attempted the scale of intervention or modification which it involved, largely due to practical difficulties, such as a lack of suitable dam sites, and the very high costs involved. Many have, on the other hand, sought to extend at least partial human control over considerably larger areas and across watersheds between river basins. Various of these schemes have now been constructed across the world from the Snowy Mountain Scheme in Australia to the Niger Dams Scheme in Nigeria and the massive Itaipu Scheme serving Brazil and Paraguay. In this chapter, we look at two case studies, one from the developed world: a complex of schemes around the Colorado River in south-west USA; and one from the lesser developed countries: the Damodar Valley Scheme in north-east India.

South-west USA and the Colorado River: case study

During the period between 1960 and 1980, the states of the south-west USA all experienced very rapid increases in population to an extent considerably greater than any other region of the USA (see Fig. 5.6). This further exacerbated the problems of water supply, which have existed throughout this region for much of this century.

	1960–1970 (%)	1970–1980 (%)
California	27.1	18.5
Nevada	71.6	63.5
Arizona	36.3	53.1
Utah	18.8	37.9
New Mexico	6.9	27.8
Wyoming	0.6	41.6
Colorado	26.0	30.7
USA	13.4	11.4

5.6 Population increase in southwestern states (1960–1980) in comparison with all of USA

The major river is the Colorado (see Figs. 5.7 and 5.8), which follows a broadly north-east to south-west course through seven states, before flowing into Mexico and to its mouth at the head of the Gulf of California. Along its 2400 km course the Colorado passes through several very deep canyons which provide excellent dam and storage reservoir sites. Inevitably, each of the seven states, and Mexico itself, wish to make their own use of the water from the Colorado and its tributaries, such that it has been necessary to reconcile these competing demands by means of an agreement now known as the 'Colorado River Compact'. The agreement, which specified the quantity of water each state was allowed to abstract from the Colorado, was only truly finalised in the mid 1960s after more than 50 years of negotiation, after a Supreme Court decision ruled in favour of Arizona following a dispute with California. To this day, the allocations (Fig. 5.7) are still the subject of controversy due to upper basin states such as Utah, Colorado and Wyoming never having used up their full entitlement in contrast to lower basin states such as California and Arizona, who have often been accused of exceeding their allotted amount and causing the River Colorado to literally 'dry up' before reaching its mouth during certain drier, low runoff periods. Considerable evidence also now exists to suggest that the allocations originally given to each state were based upon overall totals for river flow which were far higher than present day averages.

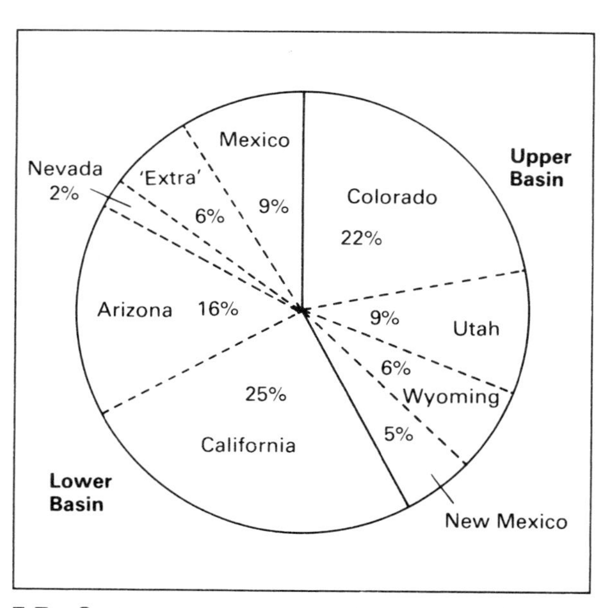

5.7 State quotas for the abstraction of water from the Colorado

The River Colorado acts as the source of fresh water for not just one but for several multi-purpose water schemes. As Fig. 5.8 shows, the headwaters of the Colorado are even drawn upon to feed the thirsty needs of irrigated farming across the natural watershed of the 'Continental Divide' in the Colorado Piedmont area to the north of Denver. The Colorado Big Thompson Project, as this scheme is called, also uses the water at several points en route to generate hydro-electric power.

Slightly further downstream, after further diversion to 'top up' the water requirements of Denver (Fig. 5.8), there are a series of irrigated areas where control of the water supply has been unified under the 'Upper Colorado Project'. The co-ordinated approach to planning and development of water use under this project has been further assisted by the construction of the Glen Canyon Dam, and the creation of Lake Powell, ensuring that the water supply and needs of the upper basin's farmers, industrialists and domestic users have been more than adequately provided for to date.

It is in the lower basin, however, that the greatest extraction of water continues to take place (see Fig. 5.7). Major dams, e.g. the Hoover Dam, Davis Dam, Parker Dam and Imperial Dam, have been built at various points on the main River itself, supplying each section of the valley immediately downstream with irrigation water (see Fig. 5.8) and generating hydro-electric power. Apart from water used to supply irrigated lands immediately adjacent to the River, large quantities are diverted both to the east, into Arizona, and to the west, to Southern California. Even further south, after what remains of the Colorado flows across the border into Mexico, even more water is extracted from the River to provide for irrigation needs in the Mexicali Valley (see Fig. 5.8).

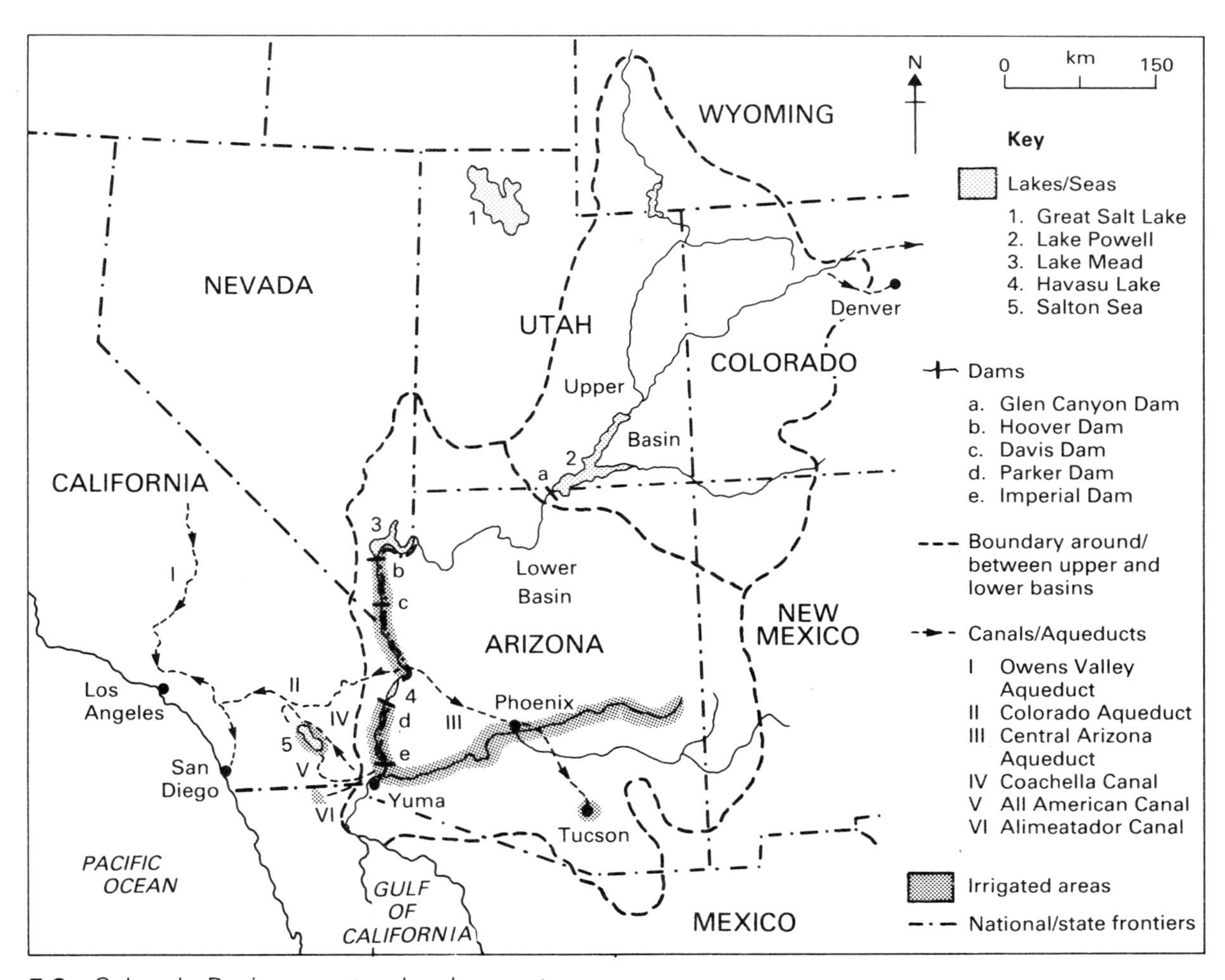

5.8 Colorado Basin — water developments

As a result of the Supreme Court decision mentioned earlier in this case study, increased quantities of water from the Colorado have been diverted east into Arizona as part of the Central Arizona Project. This project involved the construction of a canal (which was completed in 1985) from a point on the Colorado immediately to the north of the Parker Dam across the southern part of the state of Arizona (Fig. 5.8). It was originally designed to meet the water requirements of irrigated farming in a state where the ground-water reserves previously used for irrigation are rapidly being depleted and where the waters of two important tributaries of the Colorado, the Gila River and the Salt River, are already being fully utilised. Despite the fact that the scheme was originally funded to help grow food, the pressing demands of rapidly increasing urban populations, e.g. in Phoenix and Tucson, has meant that half of this water is now used to meet these needs.

Southern California is similar to Arizona in being an area with extensive irrigated farming and rapidly increasing urban population, e.g. in Los Angeles and San Diego, which places considerable demands on water from the Colorado river system. The Lake Matthews storage reservoir alone, on the outskirts of Los Angeles, receives four billion litres of water a day via the Colorado Aqueduct (completed 1941, expanded 1961) from Havasu Lake on the River Colorado to the north of Parker Dam (Fig. 5.8). This water supplements the supply from Owens Valley in the Sierra Nevada mountains, which is brought via the Los Angeles Aqueduct (built 1913) to Lake Perris, another storage reservoir to the east of Los Angeles. Future water needs for the Los Angeles–San Diego area may well be met by water transfer from northern California via the California Aqueduct under the 'State Water Project'. Further downstream still, the waters of the Colorado are diverted, at the Imperial Dam, to the north of the Mexican border, along the All-American Canal and the Coachella Canal to provide irrigation in the Imperial and Coachella Valleys around the Salton Sea.

There is no doubt that the Colorado now ranks amongst the most intensively used river courses in the world, with nine huge dams and storage reservoirs. In terms of quantity of water used, hydro-electricity is the greatest user, but it must be remembered that almost all of this water is returned to the river for further use, a fact unfortunately not true of irrigation which seriously depletes the river's flow. In the south-west USA, as in other arid and semi-arid regions of the world, irrigation is used in two distinct ways: a) to supplement the normal pattern of rainfall in 'marginal' areas; and b) to make 'the desert bloom'.

The vast increase in irrigated agriculture to over one million hectares in this area has not been without problems and, in places, irrigated land is actually going out of use due to such problems as waterlogging of surface soil, caused by poor drainage, and a build up of salts and poisons, e.g. selenium, due to the constant use of sediment-saturated Colorado irrigation water which previously would have been washed out to sea.

Damodar Valley: case study

One of the features associated with the economic development of many less developed countries is a high degree of central planning which has often been implemented through a series of 'development plans'. In India, this has been a feature of its development since it gained independence from Britain in 1947. During the first development plan (1951/2–1955/6), great emphasis was placed upon the rural economy, with a larger proportion of total expenditure (28.1%) than has been spent since going on irrigation and power schemes (Fig. 5.9). It was within the span of this first development plan that one of India's foremost multipurpose water projects, the Damodar Valley Scheme (Fig. 5.10), came into being.

In the early 1950s, the Damodar Valley was one of India's few industrial regions, with con-

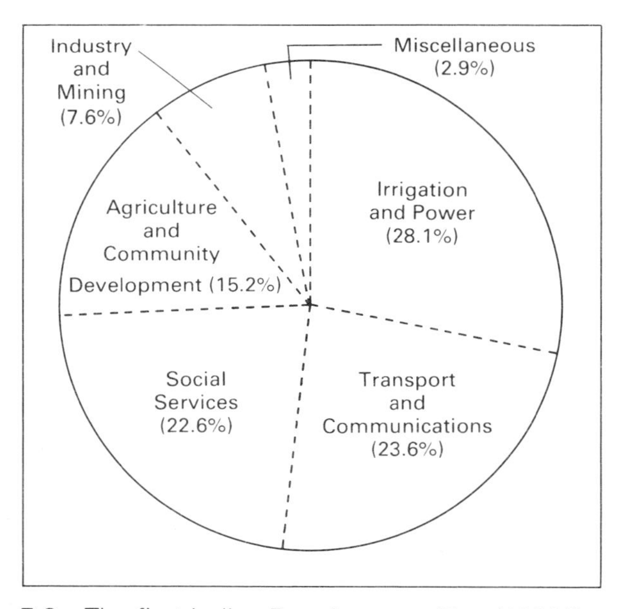

5.9 The first Indian Development Plan (1951/2–1955/6)

siderable reserves of various raw materials, e.g. copper, manganese, bauxite, iron ore, and coal. The city of Calcutta and its industrial 'suburb' of Howrah (see Fig. 5.10) lay 150 km to the east and also required large amounts of electricity. In the past, the River Damodar had been subject to unpredictable and severe flooding, such that many rural villages within the valley and further downstream near to its confluence with the Hooghly had been 'washed away' and crops had been ruined. All of these factors — the need for cheap electricity from hydro-power, the need for flood control, combined with the development plan emphasis on increasing irrigated agriculture to improve the rural economy — contributed to the obvious conclusion that the Damodar Valley was ideal for a multi-purpose water project.

The core of the Damodar Valley Scheme involved the construction of five dams with associated hydro-electric power stations at key points within the river basin (see Fig. 5.10). Upstream of each dam, a storage reservoir has been created, allowing for the capture of excess runoff in times of flood; and below the dam which lies furthest downstream, at Durgapur, a canal system has been constructed which allows for the all-year-round cultivation of crops on the fringe of the Hooghly–Ganges floodplain even during the monsoon 'dry season'.

As with all multi-purpose water schemes, there have been certain adverse effects to take account of as well: a) waterlogging and the increase in soil salinity due to irrigation water raising the water table; b) refugee problems resulting from the displacement of people due to dam and reservoir construction; and c) an increase in the prevalence of water-related diseases, e.g. malaria (reservoirs provide breeding grounds for the mosquito) and filariosis, due to the creation of vast new expanses of water.

Water transfer schemes

Interbasin water transfer has been practised in different areas of the world for some time now. It is a technique which has been used in England and Wales in the past to ensure adequate supplies of fresh water to our cities, particularly from the Lake District to Manchester and central Wales to Birmingham. As Fig. 5.11 shows, it is likely that moves will be made in future towards the creation of a National Water Grid for England and Wales, which is likely to involve interbasin transfer from areas of surplus to areas of deficit. In order to facilitate the future development of such a transfer network of rivers, aqueducts and tunnels, the regional water authorities were reorganised accord-

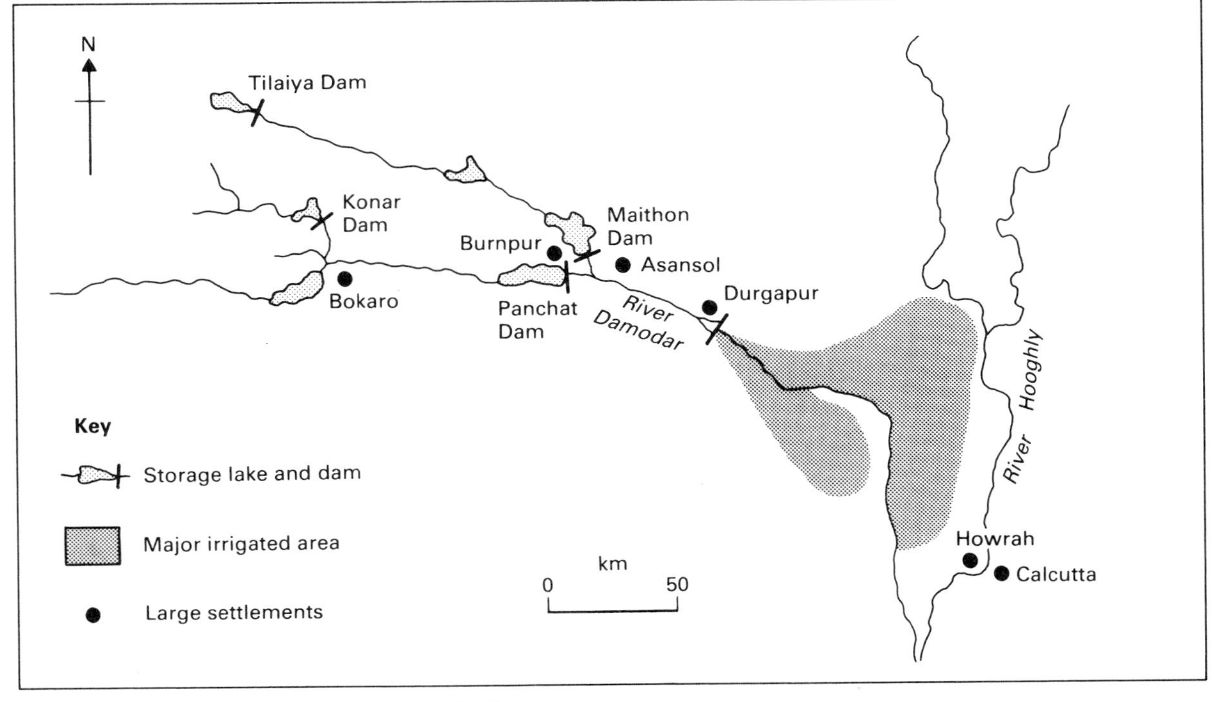

5.10 The Damodar Valley scheme, India

ing to river basin areas in the 1970s (see Fig. 5.11).

Schemes such as the National Water Grid pale into insignificance however when compared to the huge water transfer, river diversion and reversal schemes proposed for certain of the world's larger land masses. The two major examples of these schemes, NAWAPA (North American Water and Power Alliance) and the Northern Rivers Project in the USSR, both involve the transfer of fresh water from north-flowing rivers in the water surplus northern parts of these land masses to water deficit areas further south.

The NAWAPA scheme (Fig. 5.12) basically proposes the damming of the headwaters of a number of rivers in Alaska, Western Canada and North Western USA, the pump-lifting of their water into an 800 km long reservoir located in the Rocky Mountain Trench and the redistribution of this water via the Columbia/Snake River system and the Colorado River system to two aqueducts: the South West Aqueduct servicing the needs of Arizona, New Mexico and Mexico; and the Colorado Basin Aqueduct, serving California and Mexico. Various extensions eastwards to those put forward under NAWAPA have also been proposed, including: a Great Lakes Waterway, Hudson Bay Seaway, James Bay Seaway, North Dakota Barge Canal and Knob Lake Barge Canal (see Fig. 5.12).

Since the end of the last century, various large-scale water transfer schemes have been suggested in the USSR. Each of these seeks to divert the water from such north-flowing rivers as the Onega, Sukhona, Pechara and Vychegda (in European USSR) and the Ob, Irtysh and possibly even the Yenesei (in Asiatic USSR) to the semi-arid regions around the Caspian and Aral Seas (see Fig. 5.13). The most recent proposal to merit

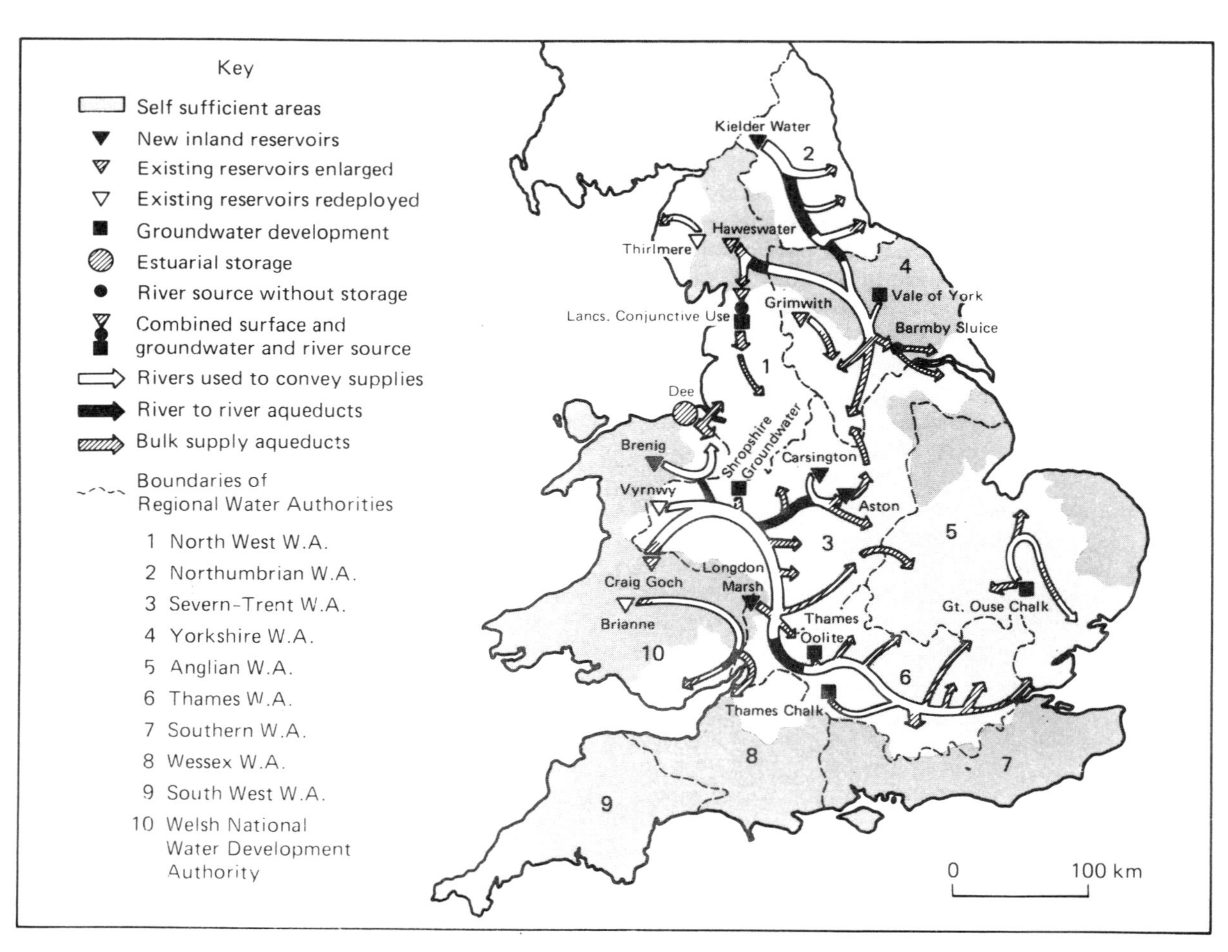

5.11 National Water Grid for England and Wales

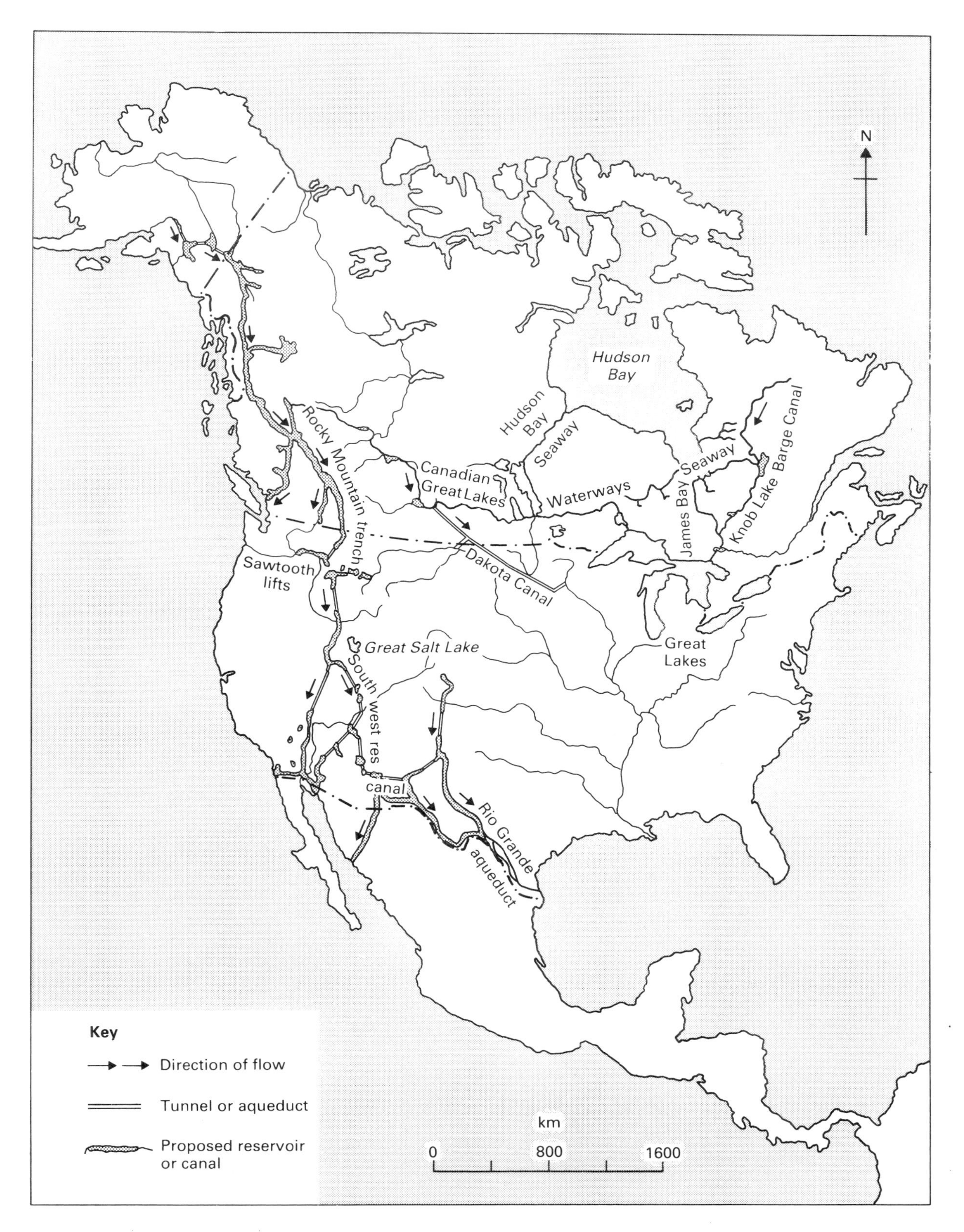

5.12 North American Water and Power Alliance Scheme

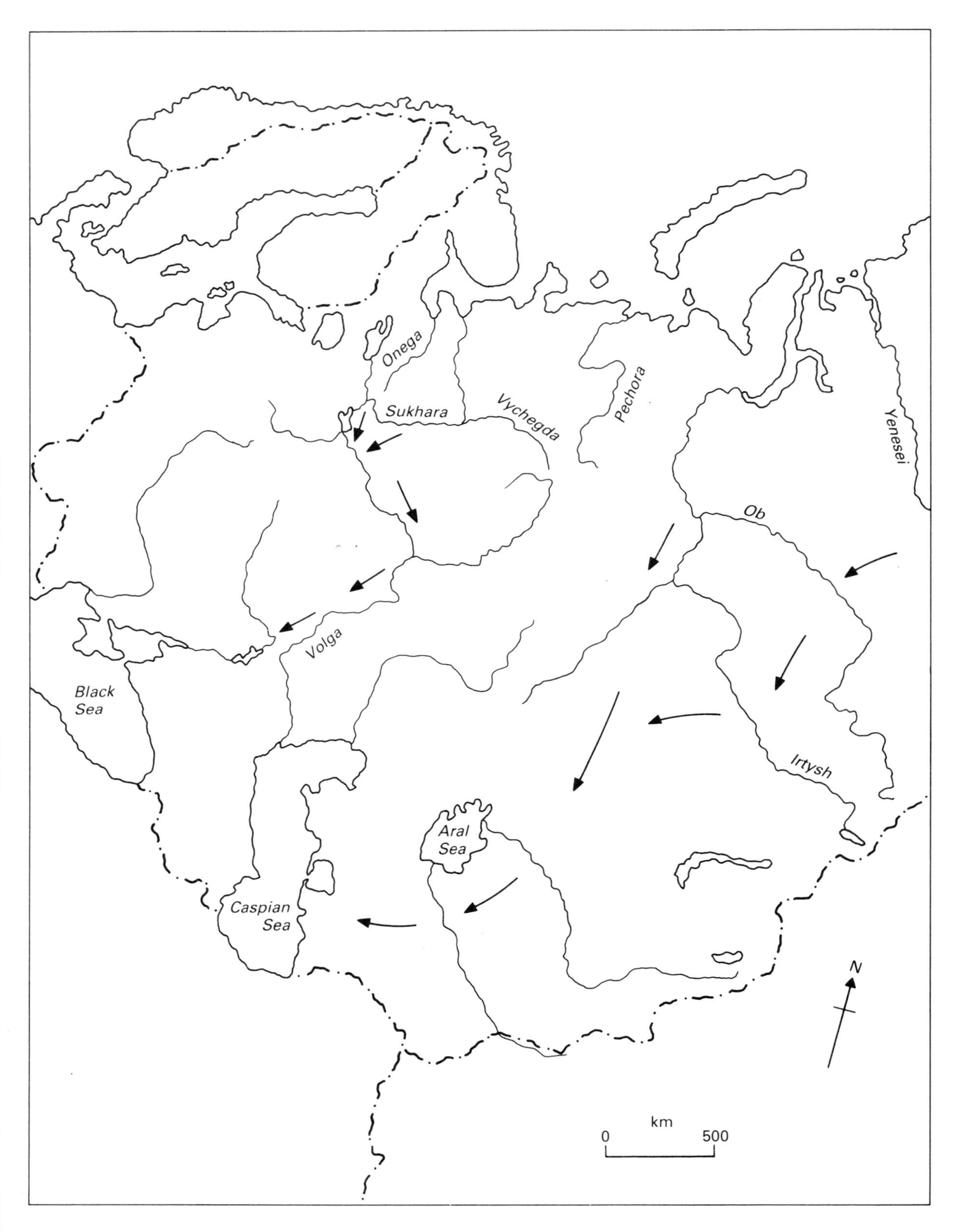

5.13 Possible river diversions in USSR

serious consideration was the Northern Rivers Project. This project was divided into two phases, the first of which proposed to divert waters from the Onega, the Pechara and their tributaries into the Volga by means of a network of dams, canals and locks. The second, and much more ambitious phase proposed to divert part of the flow of the rivers Ob and Irtysh in Western Siberia southwards to Central Asia and Kazakhstan.

One of the reasons why the NAWAPA proposal has not yet got beyond the planning stage, is because of its political implications. Under the NAWAPA, Canada would stand to lose vast quantities of one of its major national assets to the USA, whose economic domination it is trying to lessen. Apart from the political aspect of NAWAPA, the environmental consequences of both NAWAPA and the Northern Rivers Project could prove horrendous. In particular, both schemes would result in a substantial reduction in fresh water flowing into the Arctic Ocean with consequent effects on the ice-cap and possible climatic change on a worldwide scale. The March 1986 announcement from the Soviet Union that the Northern Rivers Project had been shelved, largely because of its possible environmental impact, recognised the need to very seriously consider all aspects of such large-scale water transfer schemes before very carefully planning if they should be allowed to proceed at all.

6. Comment upon the relative efficiency of traditional and modern methods of irrigation as means of a) water transfer and b) water delivery to plants (see Fig. 5.2).

7. Referring to Fig. 5.3 and particular examples you have studied, describe and explain the most important ways in which humans interfere in the water cycle within a river basin.

8. Select one example of a major multi-purpose river basin development scheme in the developed world and contrast it with a similar scheme in the less developed countries.

9. 'Multi-purpose water schemes can have negative as well as positive effects'. With reference to particular case studies known to you, describe and account for any negative social and/or environmental effects.

10. a) From the evidence on Figs. 5.12 and 5.13, which regions within North America and the USSR can be identified as: i) water surplus and ii) water deficit areas.
    b) Both the NAWAPA and Northern Rivers proposals involved very large scale water transfer. In both cases outline how it was proposed to greatly increase the water available in existing river systems.
    c) Suggest why the NAWAPA scheme has never got beyond the planning stage and the Northern Rivers Project has now 'been shelved'.

6
The forests

The use of forest resources

The biogeography of natural forests has already been discussed (chapters 3 and 4) and this chapter is concerned mainly with human use of forested areas and with the resulting ecological consequences. Although forests account for about one-third of the world's land area, the impact of technological development particularly during the last 200 years has meant that very few areas of natural woodland remain. It is estimated that before large-scale disturbance by people, forests and woodlands occupied an area approaching 6000 million hectares, although latest estimates put the current figure at less than 4000 million hectares: a decline of over 30%.

Human use of forests can be classified into two main categories: consumptive and non-consumptive (Fig. 6.1). In recent years the commercial felling of trees has increased substantially and it has become clear that forest ecosystems have been coming under increased pressure to meet growing demand for forest products. At the same time, with population increases, much woodland has been clear-felled to increase the land available for commercial farming. But forests are more than just stands of trees — their importance in land and water resource management is crucial

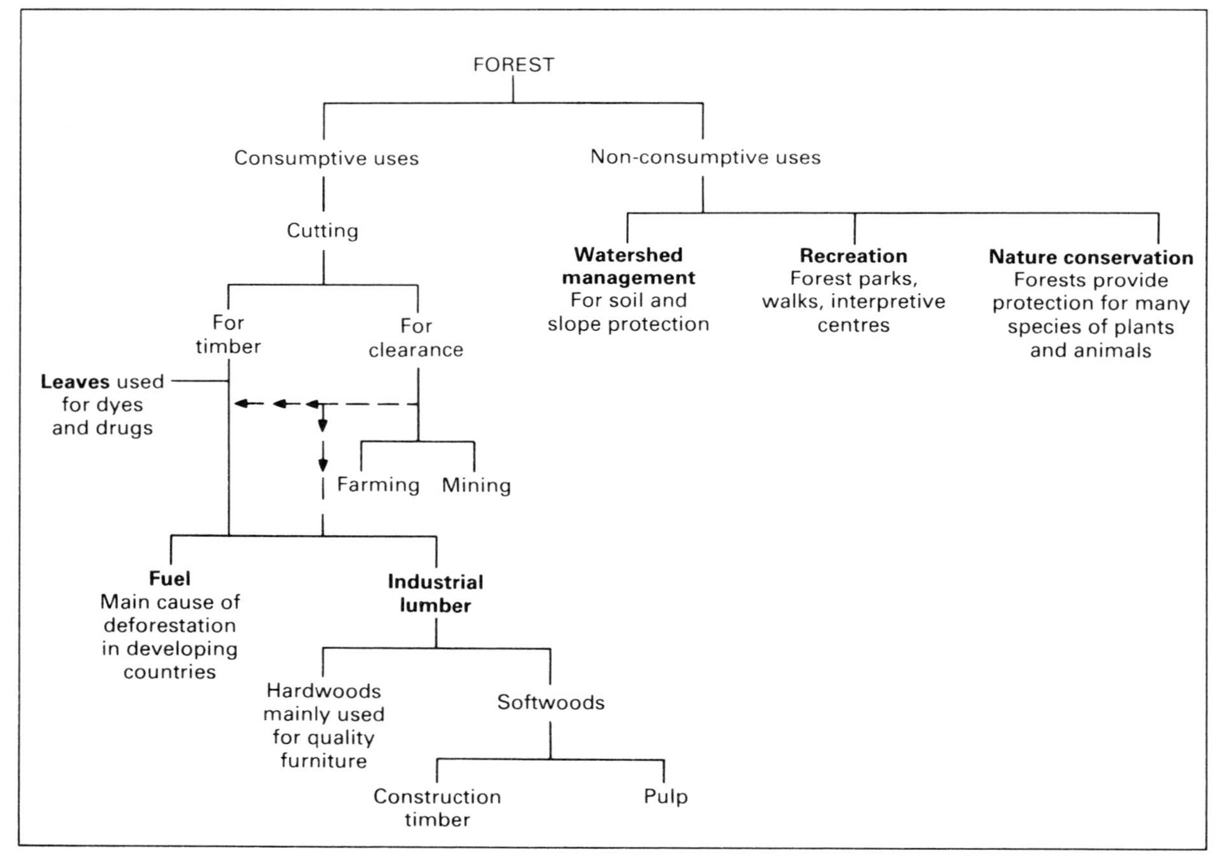

6.1 Use of forest resources

and involves a complex system of interdependent processes and ecosystems. In fact, forests are at the meeting point of air, water and land resources.

Forests are natural filters of the atmosphere: their evapotranspiration processes are a vital part of the hydrological cycle adding to air humidity and affecting micro-climates: protecting against frosts in some valleys. They control both surface and ground-water flow and regulate the water table by their collecting, storing, filtering and distribution. In terms of land resources, tree roots bind soil particles, prevent erosion and landslips and break the force of winds, giving protection to both soil and crops.

1. Describe the main uses of forest resources and explain the importance of trees in land and water resource management.

Coniferous forests (taiga)

The vast **boreal forests** of the northern hemisphere stretch in a broad latitudinal belt (Fig. 3.9a, p. 28), occupying over 11% of the earth's land surface, from Alaska across Canada and Scandinavia to Siberia in the USSR. They consist mainly of coniferous trees such as pine and spruce, but on their southern edges they may include aspen, birch and poplar. Trees often grow in stands of single species which can be relatively easily cut and transported; as a result many of these areas have developed important timber industries.

Commercial forestry in British Columbia: case study

Trees in Canada occupy about 40% of the total land area and in 1983 exports of Canadian forest products, mainly to the USA and Japan, earned US$10 240 million, over twice as much as Sweden, the nearest competitor. It is estimated that about a quarter of Canada's forests — mostly in the northern interior, have not yet even been inventoried.

Within Canada, one of the most important forest areas is the coastal area of British Columbia which accounts for about 40% of all cut timber production. Throughout the province, the species and size of tree differ widely as a consequence of the relief and climate (Fig. 6.2). The coast forest region occupying the western slopes of the Cascade Mountains, the coast ranges, Queen Charlotte Islands and Vancouver Island, is mild and humid (rainfall up to 2500 mm p.a.) with trees growing up to sixty metres in height and two metres in diameter. Moving inland rainfall decreases, but production in the interior has expanded rapidly in recent years as new forest technology has made the harvesting of the smaller sized timber more economic and demand for this type of wood from pulp and paper mills has increased rapidly.

Good **forest management** is essential to maintain the economic, ecological and recreational value of the forests. To the first fur trappers and gold prospectors who arrived in British Columbia, the forests must have seemed endless, causing problems for transport and the building of settlements. There followed the 'timber boom' as the new railways opened up new markets across the continent, and the Panama Canal brought the wood-hungry European markets within reach. Although British Columbia's forests remain impressive in extent, a century of lumbering has taken its toll, and the forest area has been reduced to make way for roads, railways, housing, industry and shopping centres. Apart from the economic effects of a diminished forest base, there have been effects on wildlife, water resources and recreation.

The British Columbia Ministry of Forests is responsible for about 94% of all woodland in the province and its forest management system, called the **Silviculture** Programme is outlined in Fig. 6.3. The programme has three main aims:

1. To maintain the natural productivity of forest sites by using proper harvesting practices.
2. To ensure that new, secondary forests replace those denuded by logging, fire or pests.
3. To produce the biggest and healthiest trees as quickly as possible.

The main challenge for the forestry industry is to make the transition from harvesting old growth to obtaining the best yields from well-managed secondary forests to meet future demand for timber, whilst at the same time meeting increasing demands for recreation and conservation. The future management of the forests will have to take account of the economic, environmental and social benefits which the trees bring to the province, and try to achieve a balance between these, whilst doing so on a reduced forest area.

Although timber resources, properly managed and harvested as in the British Columbian Silviculture Programme, are classified as **renewable resources**, there are signs that our forests are under increasing threats from new sources, in both the developed and developing worlds. In Latin America and Asia, despite increased large-scale **deforestation** by commercial interests, the major problem remains the traditional cutting down of timber for fuelwood and to create cropland — although the increased population pressure now makes this much more acute. In Europe however, there is a new and potentially much more serious problem: **acidification**.

6.2 British Columbia — forest resources

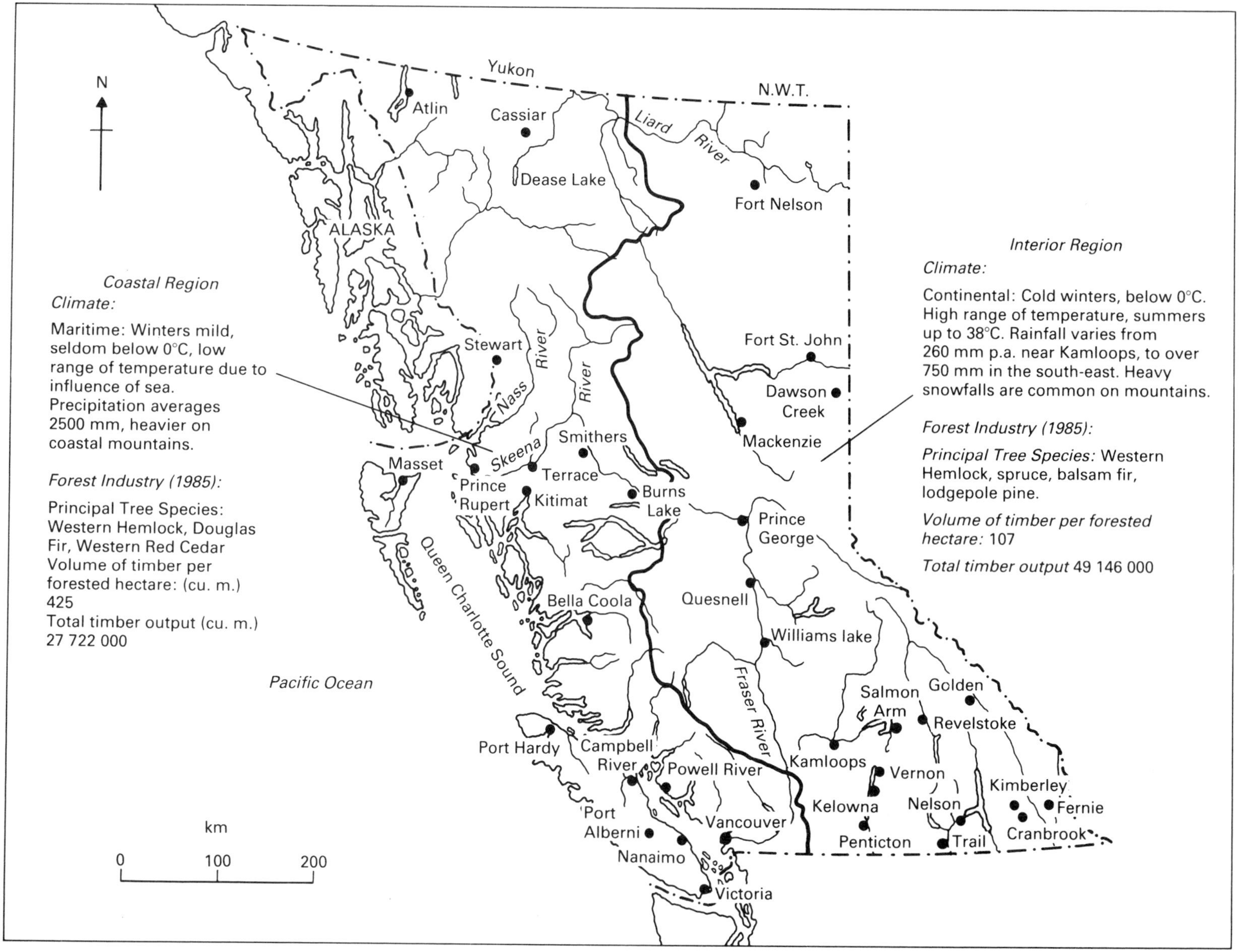
N
Yukon
N.W.T.
Atlin
Cassiar
Dease Lake
Liard River
Fort Nelson
ALASKA
Stewart
Nass River
Skeena River
Smithers
Terrace
Masset
Prince Rupert
Kitimat
Burns Lake
Fort St. John
Dawson Creek
Mackenzie
Prince George
Queen Charlotte Sound
Bella Coola
Quesnell
Williams lake
Fraser River
Salmon Arm
Golden
Revelstoke
Kamloops
Vernon
Kelowna
Penticton
Nelson
Trail
Kimberley
Fernie
Cranbrook
Port Hardy
Campbell River
Powell River
Port Alberni
Nanaimo
Vancouver
Victoria
Pacific Ocean
km
0
100
200
Coastal Region
Climate:
Maritime: Winters mild, seldom below 0°C, low range of temperature due to influence of sea. Precipitation averages 2500 mm, heavier on coastal mountains.
Forest Industry (1985):
Principal Tree Species: Western Hemlock, Douglas Fir, Western Red Cedar
Volume of timber per forested hectare: (cu. m.) 425
Total timber output (cu. m.) 27 722 000
Interior Region
Climate:
Continental: Cold winters, below 0°C. High range of temperature, summers up to 38°C. Rainfall varies from 260 mm p.a. near Kamloops, to over 750 mm in the south-east. Heavy snowfalls are common on mountains.
Forest Industry (1985):
Principal Tree Species: Western Hemlock, spruce, balsam fir, lodgepole pine.
Volume of timber per forested hectare: 107
Total timber output 49 146 000

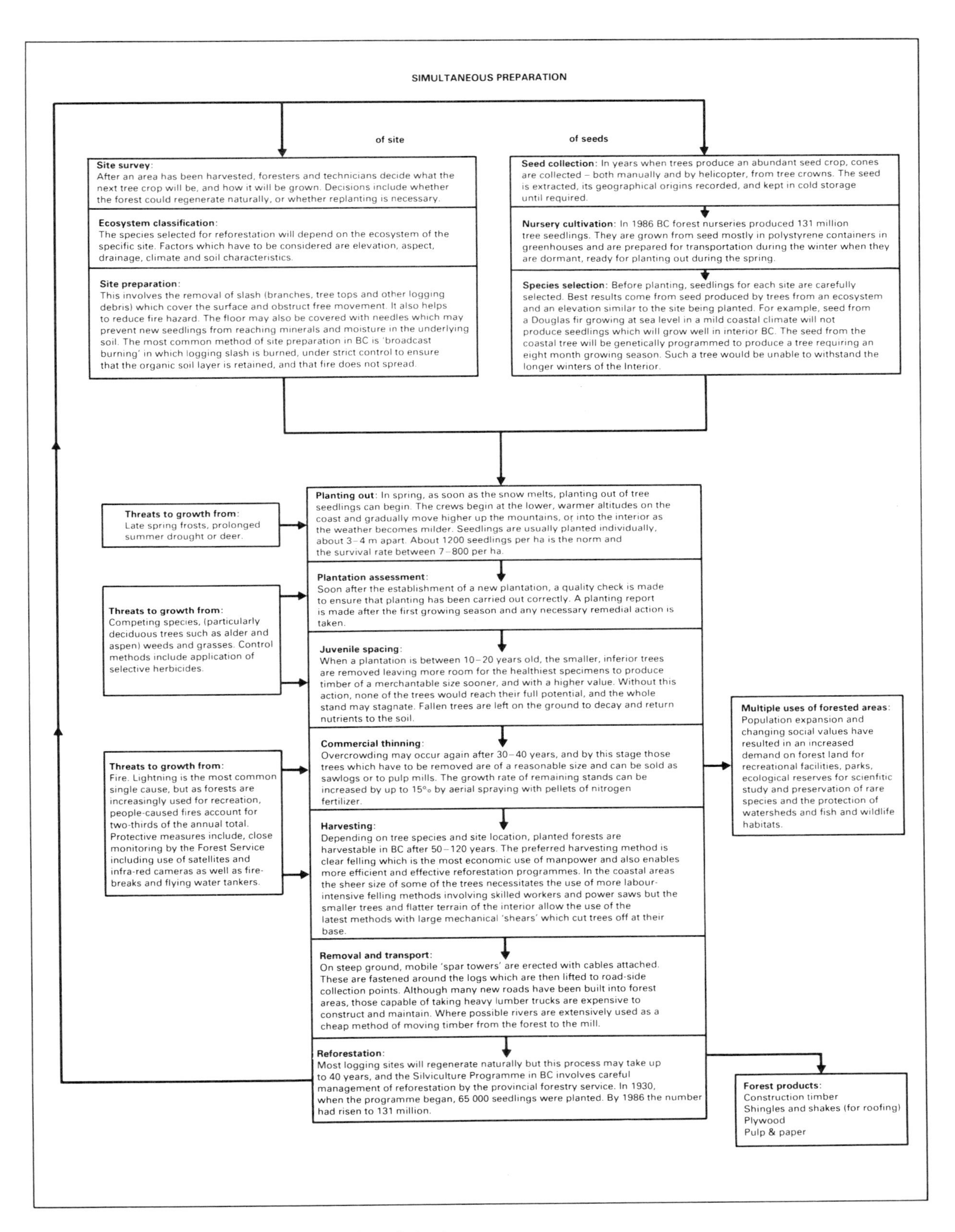

6.3 British Columbia's forests — the silviculture programme

German forests — the acidification threat: case study

The Germans call it 'waldsterben' — the dying forest syndrome. The first signs began to appear during the 1970s on fir trees in southern Germany — branches hung limply and turned yellow. Needles fell and were not replaced, the trees became bald at the top, whilst at the base tiny new branches or 'anxiety shoots' appeared. The result was a weakening of the trees' natural defences — almost like a forest version of the AIDS virus — leaving them prone to attack from frost, drought and natural parasites.

Since then, the problem has spread across much of central Europe affecting places as far apart as Sweden, Italy and Czechoslovakia. It is no longer confined to coniferous trees, but is also affecting oak and beech. In 1985 *TIME* magazine claimed that 'Europe now faces one of the most serious environmental catastrophes of modern times' (Fig. 6.5).

The damage is particularly dramatic in the West German forests — in 1982 less than 8% of the country's 7.4 million ha of forest were affected. By 1984, a survey found that over 50% of forests were affected and, in the central and southern states which contain the highest proportion of forests, some areas showed a rate of 85% of severe damage (see Fig. 6.4).

The causes are a matter of dispute amongst scientists, but the most convincing explanation points to an increase in air pollution, particularly of sulphur dioxide and nitrogen oxides. These originate from various sources (Fig. 6.5) and mix together in the atmosphere, when combined with oxygen and sunlight, nitrogen oxides turns into **ozone**. These chemicals return to earth in the form of rain, snow, mist and dust: **acid rain**. The airborne pollution first settles on the crowns or tops of trees and precipitation filters down to the root systems leaching out key nutrients from the soil. Leaves and needles are also attacked, disrupting systems of transpiration and photosynthesis and resulting in discoloration, premature ageing and death. In high-altitude Alpine forests where sunshine is particularly intense, **ozone** prevalent, and acid mists common, forest damage is often most severe.

Public concern over the fate of German forests has made the problem a major national issue. West Germany has passed strict pollution control laws aimed at reducing SO_2 emissions by half by 1993. New coal burning power stations have gas desulphurisation equipment installed, and nitrous oxide emissions from car exhausts are to be reduced by the introduction of lead-free petrol. In order to encourage motorists to buy cars equipped to use this type of fuel, it is to carry a reduced rate of tax.

6.4 The effects of Acid Rain — Black Forest

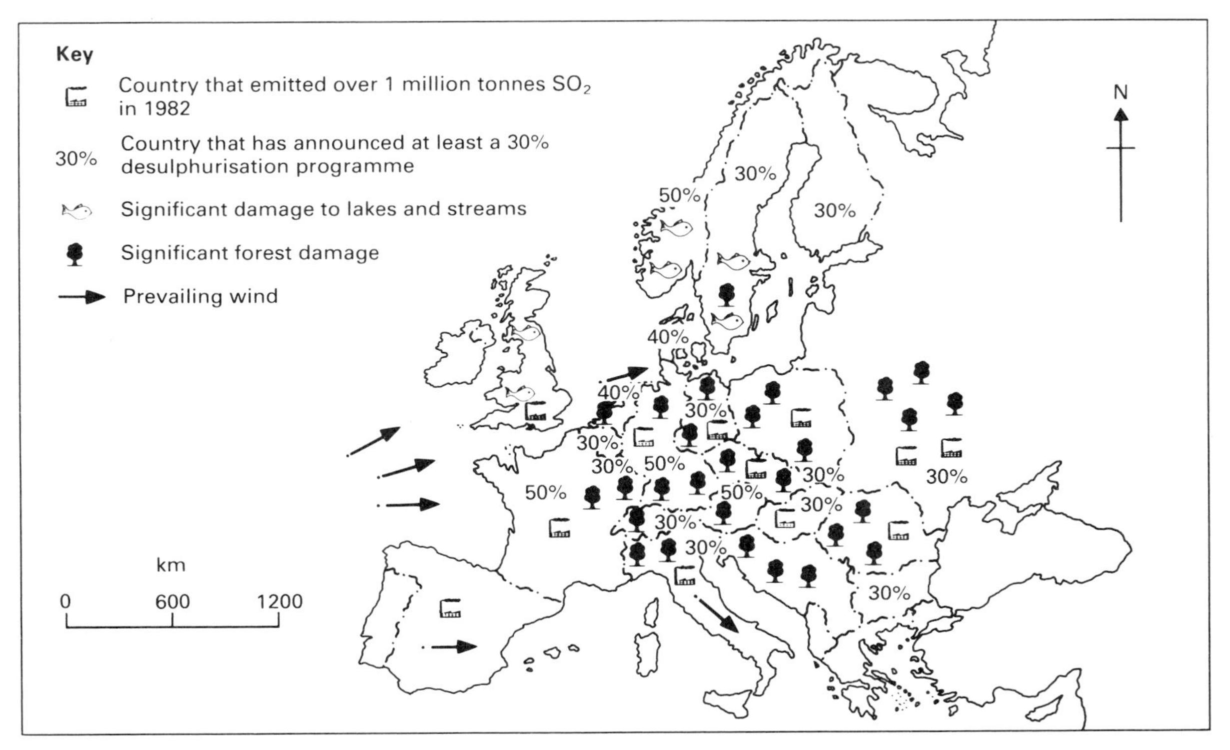

6.5 Acid rain in Europe

The economic implications of forest dieback in West Germany could run into several thousand million pounds. Damaged timber is already reaching the market in high volumes, thereby reducing prices, and in the long term the premature felling of affected trees could result in a shortage of timber and loss of jobs in forestry and wood-processing industries. The loss of trees is also affecting several areas which relied on the recreational use of the forests such as Bavaria in the south and the Harz Mountains near the border with East Germany. Other effects are already being seen in Alpine areas where the trees are no longer a protection against avalanches and ecological changes — soil erosion, increased rainwater runoff rates and disruption to forest wildlife are already in evidence.

Whilst the measures taken by the West German government are important, their impact on the problem is likely to be minimal without much greater international co-operation. Already, many countries have announced a desulphurisation programme (see Fig. 6.5), but Britain, the largest generator of SO_2 in Western Europe, has not signed. In 1984 it was estimated that 28% of the 5.1 million tonnes produced, mainly by coal burning power stations, were borne by the prevailing south-westerly winds to other countries, particularly Scandinavia and West Germany.

2. Using an atlas and Fig. 6.2 describe and explain the distribution of coniferous forests:
   a) within Canada
   b) within British Columbia.

3. What do you understand by the term silviculture? What are the aims of the British Columbian Silviculture Programme and why is it necessary?

4. Using Fig. 6.3 describe the management of a typical forested area in British Columbia using the following headings:
   Site preparation, Seed preparation, Planting, Cultivation methods, Extraction, Timber uses, Conservation methods.

5. What are the main threats to forestry in British Columbia and what methods are employed to combat these problems?

6. Identify and explain the main causes of acid rain in Europe.

7. Describe the effects of acidification on West German forests.

8. What steps have been taken by the West German government to reduce acidification? Explain why these are likely to be only a limited success.

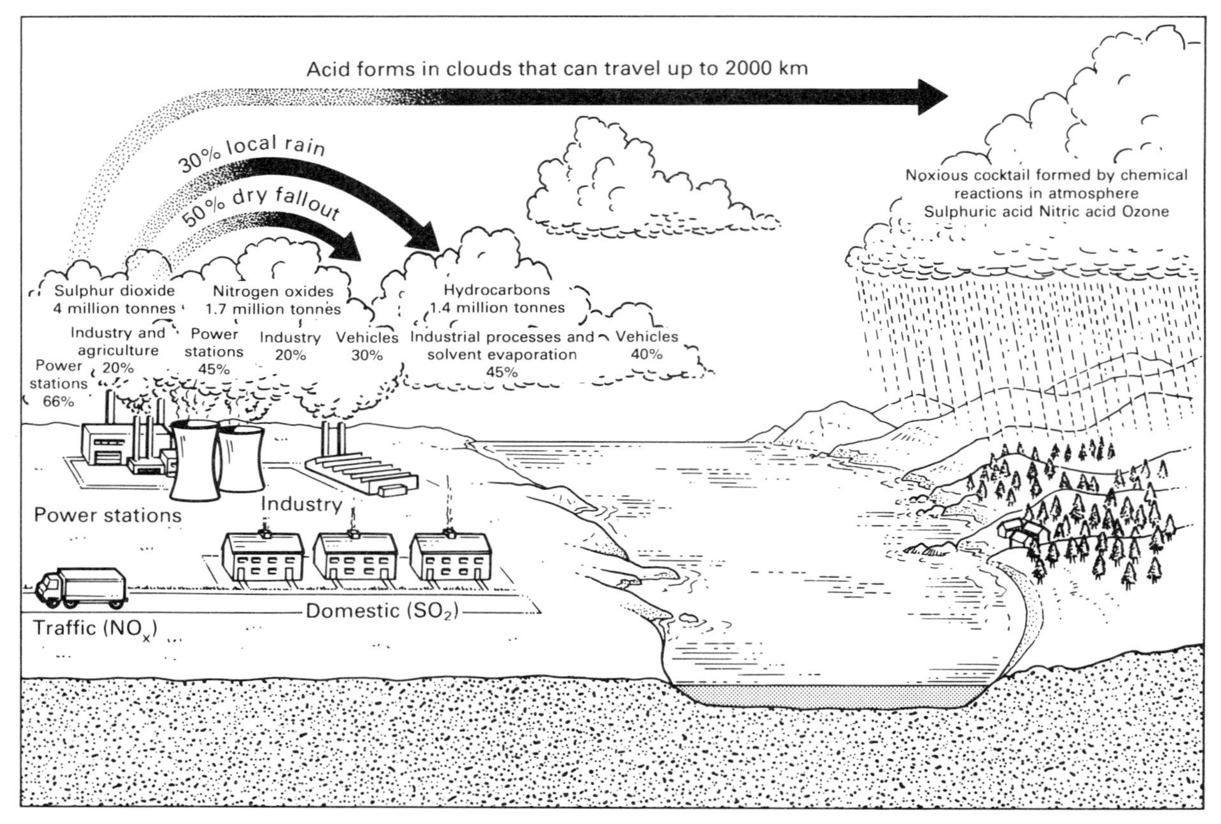

6.6 Acid rain formation

Tropical rain forests

Tropical rain forests cover about 7% of the world's land surface, a total of 900 million ha which is about the size of the USA. The world distribution is shown in Fig. 3.3a), p. 22, with most concentrated in Brazil (33%), Indonesia and Zaire (10% each). The importance of these forests cannot be overestimated — their genetic diversity is of particular significance. Whereas a hectare of temperate forest might contain up to 10–15 tree species, the same area of Amazonian rain forest might hold up to 200. They support about half of the world's plant and animal species, but the Global 2000 Report prepared for the US President in 1980 estimated that one million TRF species are likely to be extinct by the end of this century. This loss is one of the consequences of deforestation in tropical rain forest areas which is now considered by many authorities to be the world's most pressing land-use problem (Fig. 6.7). From the viewpoint of some of the governments of these countries, however, the conservation issues often take a low priority behind national security, economic development and socio-political considerations.

Development issues in Amazonia: case study

The vast Amazonian rain forest or **selvas**, covers an area of 6 million km^2 — twice the size of Western Europe and the largest of all of the tropical rain forests in the world. A large part of the forest (3.6 million km^2) lies within Brazil, occupying over 40% of the country's area, yet containing only 4% of population, and generating less than 2% of Brazilian national income. Much of the area remains unexplored and it is only recently, with the aid of remote-sensing satellite imagery that it has been possible to map the territory with any accuracy.

Early attempts at large-scale developments in the rain forest met with failure due to a combination of inaccessibility, climate, disease and other factors (Fig. 6.8). The late 19th century 'rubber boom' — to meet demand for both tyres and for electrical installations saw population in the Amazon increase by five times and saw the growth of Manaus and Belem as the region's first urban centres. The boom was short-lived as fatalities from malaria increased and the successful development of rubber plantations in Malaya led to the collapse of the Brazilian rubber economy.

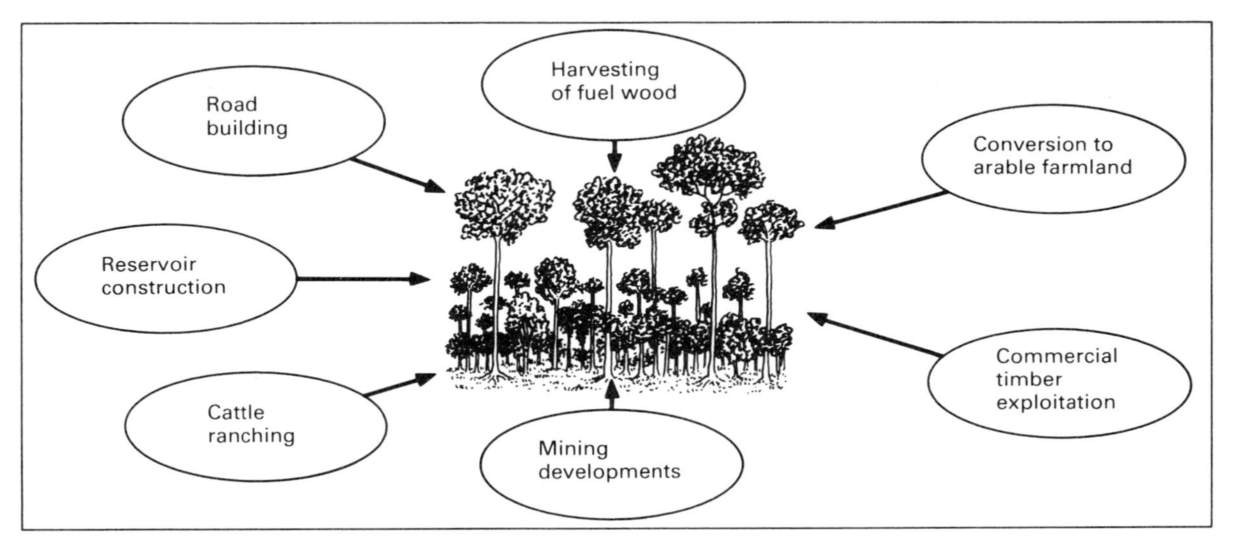

6.7a Deforestation pressures on moist tropical forest

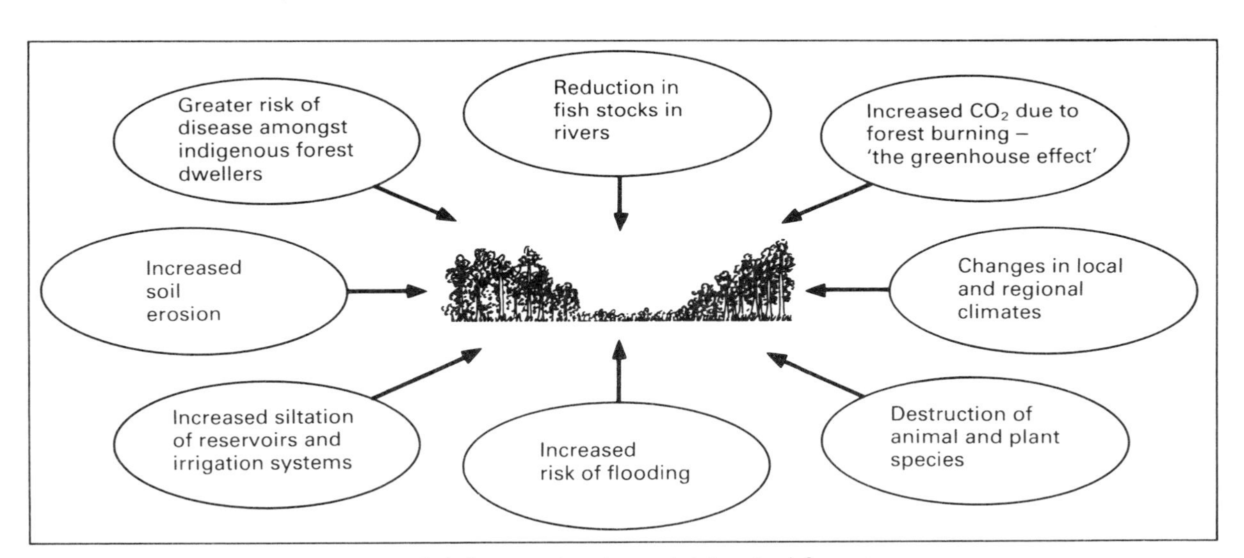

6.7b Possible consequences of deforestation in moist tropical forests

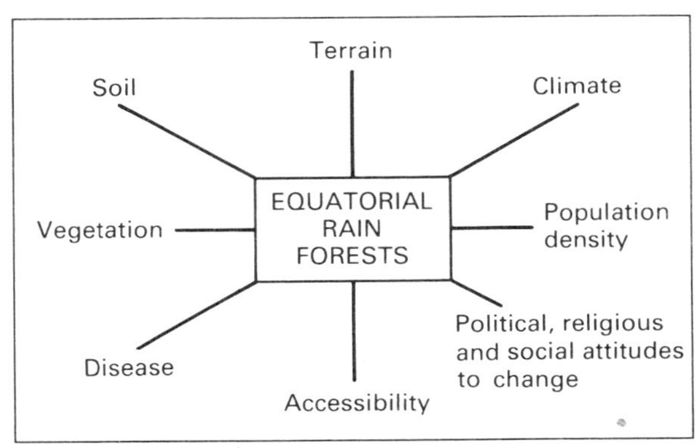

6.8 Factors limiting development in Equatorial rainforests

A later attempt by the Ford Motor Company to establish rubber plantations in the Tapajos valley in 1927 also failed as large-scale forest clearance resulted in widespread soil exhaustion and erosion.

The Amazon forest area came to be regarded in Brazil as a 'valuable asset going to waste' and in 1966 the SUDAM (Superintendancy of the Amazon) development authority was established in an attempt to encourage and co-ordinate the development of the region. An increasing aim of the Brazilian government has been its desire to occupy its strategic northern and western frontiers, fuelled by suspicion of neighbouring states, as well as an increasing realisation of the immense resource base of the Amazon region.

Developments since 1966 have been controversial. On the one hand a large number of schemes has been undertaken by both the Brazilian government and commercial interests most notably the Polamazonia Programme launched in 1974 (Fig. 6.9) to spread developments throughout the region. On the other, these have been met with severe criticism from conservationists who regard the developments as piecemeal, unplanned and ill-supported. Certainly, it would be fair to say that there has been a number of expensive failures and that many of the developments have caused disruption and degradation to the forest ecosystem.

Infrastructural developments

The inaccessibility of the Amazon region has always been regarded as a fundamental obstacle to development. Whilst this is undoubtedly true, new communication links have not proved to be the entire solution to the region's problems. There are now over 2000 km of trunk roads and more than 1500 km of rural link roads in Amazonia. Eleven new airports and six new ports have been built and electricity capacity vastly increased. The Trans-Amazon Highway (Fig. 6.10) is perhaps symbolic of the whole concept of Brazil's Amazonian development. In 1968 the decision was taken to construct this 6370 km long road with the primary objective of encouraging the 'productive occupation' of the region by up to

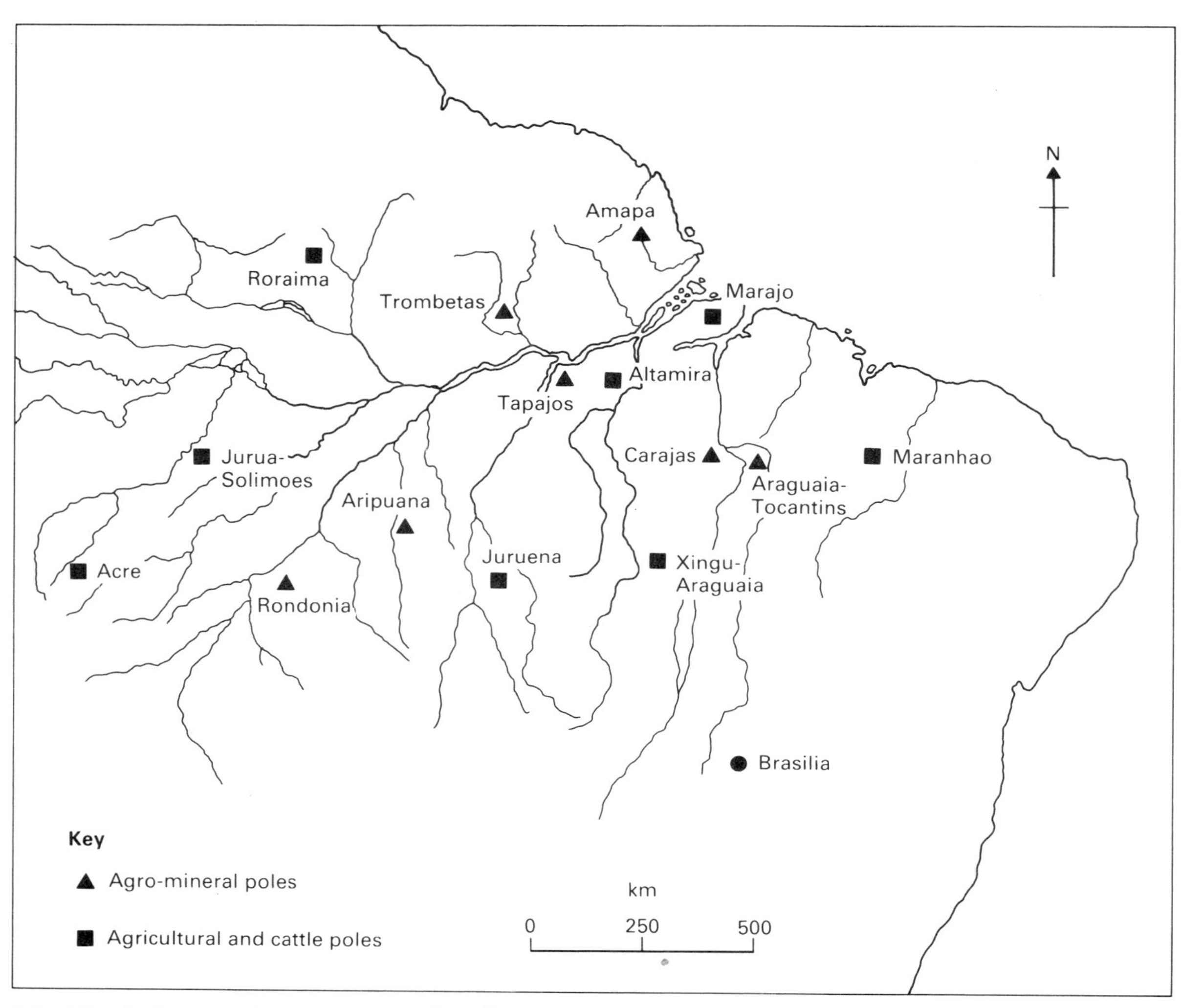

6.9 The Polamazonia programme, Brazil

500 000 people. Running from the north-east coast to the Peruvian border it was to be a key element in promoting development in Amazonia. The new road was to serve as a 'growth corridor', opening up the rain forest for economic development, encouraging new settlements and offering new marketing opportunities for the farmers who were to be encouraged to clear land adjacent to the road. Although there has been some development, mainly concentrated around certain 'growth poles' identified by the government, it has been generally sporadic. The road itself has never been completely finished with some river crossings abandoned. The climate makes maintenance an economic nightmare for the government, with dust-clouds alternating with pot-holes and quagmires. The economic importance of the road is also questionable. The simple fact of linking two parts of Brazil did not create an immediate upsurge in trade. The farmers attracted into the Amazon were promised technical and financial assistance which almost invariably never materialised and therefore most had to work hard to produce enough to achieve a subsistence level for themselves and their families, seldom were they able to produce a surplus for sale. Even when farmers were fortunate enough to find themselves allocated plots of fertile soil, the lack of markets and transport during the rainy season sometimes resulted in up to 40% of crops harvested having to be left to rot. The trade problem was perhaps best summarised by the local roads director for Amazonas who commented that the road south from Manaus to Porto Velho made economic sense because it provided a link between an area with a high consumption rate of raw materials

6.10 Trans–Amazon Highway

(the south) to an area which provided a small but growing market for manufactured goods (the Amazon). He said, '. . . but this is not the case with the Transamazon: because the north-east consumes very little of what we produce, and produces very little of what we consume.'

Small-scale farming

Traditionally, the lowland Amerindians of the Amazon Basin, such as the Boro and Nambiquara developed a form of subsistence farming which, given the low population density, allowed a balance between their own basic needs, and the capacity of the rain forest ecosystem to supply them and regenerate (Fig. 6.11). After clearing the rain forest vegetation and digging ashes into the soil to act as a fertilizer, a variety of crops such as yams and manioc were grown, but without the tree cover and forest nutrient cycle, the soil

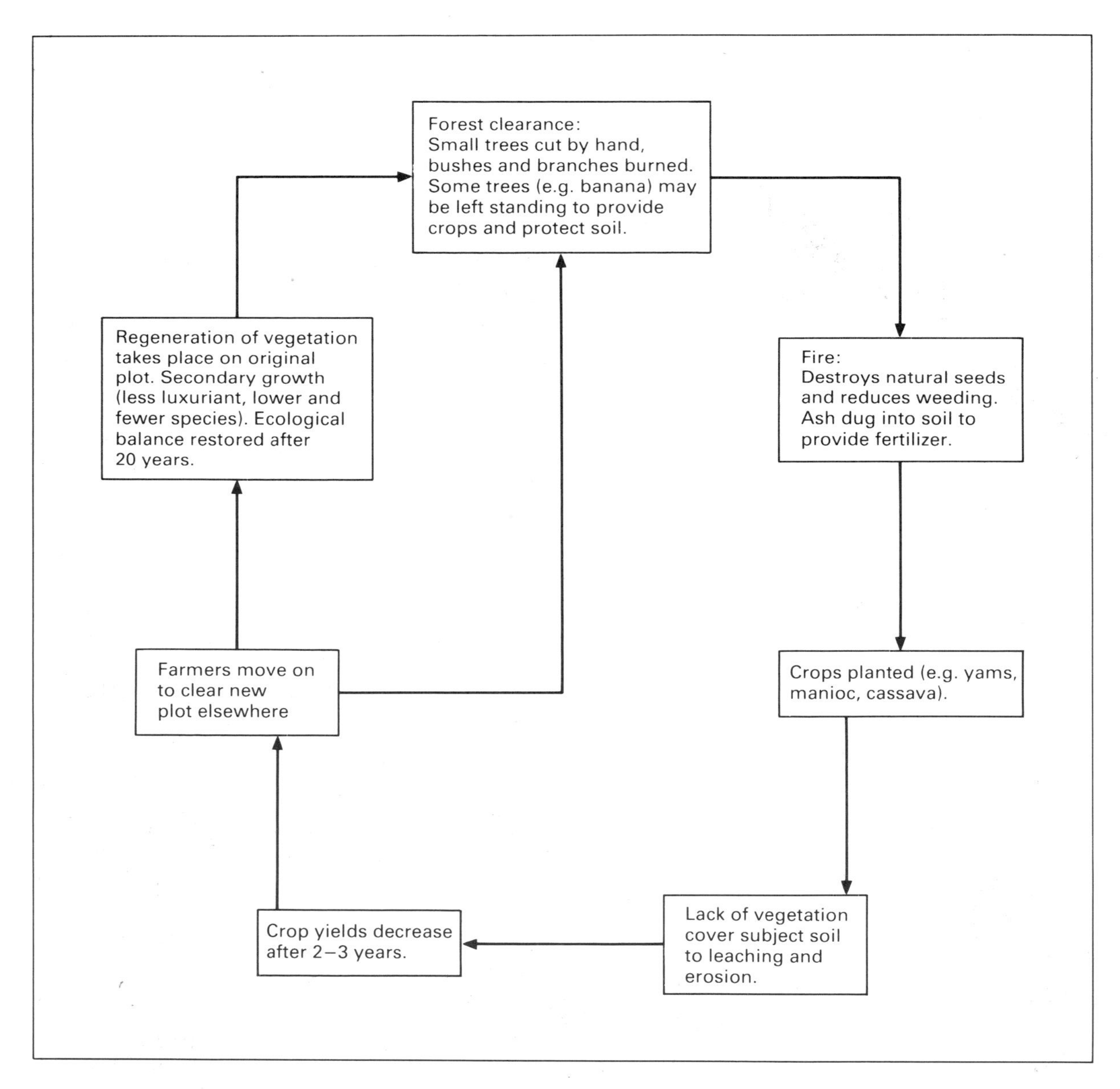

6.11 Shifting Agriculture in the Amazon rainforest

soon lost its fertility and became subject to erosion. As soil productivity declined, the farmers moved on to clear a new patch after two or three years. The abandoned clearances were left fallow for about ten years allowing the growth of **secondary forest**. Many forest dwellers preferred to re-work these areas rather than the **primary forest** because they were easier to clear and contained more useful vegetation for food and construction: this relieved the pressure on the primary forest and minimised its destruction. This system was sustainable only at low population densities (2 or 3 people per km^2) and problems arose in Amazonia with the Brazilian government's policy of encouraging the movement of landless migrants into the Amazon forest from other parts of the country as part of its development strategy. Leaving behind the drought-stricken north-east and the huge mechanised farms of southern Brazil, the movement into the Amazon has been facilitated by construction of roads such as the Trans-Amazon, and has raised the population/land ratio. Legislation encourages settlers to clear away the forest — land rights depend on cutting down trees to grow crops or sow pasture, but all too often the newcomers lacked the expertise of the traditional forest dwellers. Once the dense rain forest is removed and farmed it becomes infertile after a few years and reverts to secondary forest growth. Instead of leaving adequate fallow time, the land in some areas has been completed degraded, making it quite useless for either agriculture or forestry.

Large-scale land development

Two kinds of landholdings have increased in number in the Amazon since the 1960s. The first is those under 10 ha (see above); the second is those of over 10 000 ha. These massive deforestations, accounting for about one-third of all clearances in the Amazon annually, are mainly controlled by a group called the Association of Impresarios of the Amazon (AIA) which represents over 300 business organisations many of which are multi-national corporations. These include the Brazilian subsidiaries of companies such as Volkswagen, Xerox and Nixdorf Computers but some of the major Brazilian banks, such as Brandesco are also involved. Many of these groups obviously see land developments in the Amazon as a good financial investment with excellent profit potential. Land prices are very low, government incentives are available and profits can often be made in the few years before the land loses its fertility. The AIA group alone aim to develop about one-third of the Amazon (1.5 million km^2) in coming years, giving Brazil potentially the largest area of farmland on earth.

The main use of the cleared land is as pasture for cattle ranches — despite the fact that ecologists generally agree that conversion of rain forest to pasture is the worst possible use of the land. Weeds are a constant problem and burning is necessary to remove them. Even so, between 10–15% of cattle are lost due to eating toxic weeds and the compacting of soil by animal hooves encourages the onset of erosion. Even with careful management, most ranches have to be abandoned after five to seven years.

The international connections go deeper — the main export route for the cheap beef produced is to North America for hamburgers, tinned meat and petfood where the price of home grown beef has soared in recent years. There are signs that the ecological price paid by Brazil to turn forests into hamburgers is at last being recognised: Brazil's environment minister has admitted that ranching in Amazonia has proved to be a 'disaster'.

Energy resources

Hydro-electricity schemes are associated with the development of Amazonia's vast mineral reserves. Certainly, the development of water power makes much less impact on the rain forest than charcoal or wood-fuelled power, but large-scale projects such as the Tucurui Dam on the Tocantins River (Fig. 6.9) with its associated 2400 km^2 reservoir can have a serious effect on the fresh-water ecosystem. The Tucurui scheme is part of a US$ 60 billion plan to develop the mineral resources of the Serra dos Carajas involving the supply of power to aluminium refineries, copper smelters and to the Brazilian national grid. Ecologists argue that despite the low gradient of the Amazon and its tributaries, the volume of water in the rivers (more water flows through the mouth of the Amazon in a day than through the Thames in a year!) could be used to develop run-of-the river schemes involving no reservoirs and virtually no environmental impact.

Mineral resources

Amazonia's known mineral reserves are vast with major deposits of bauxite, iron ore, tin, copper and manganese. Until recently, the development of ore bodies and transportation of minerals was a major problem due to environmental conditions but as world demand for metals continues to increase, so prices rise to levels which make mining developments in areas such as Amazonia economically viable.

One of the largest deposits occurs in the Serra dos Carajas, near the Tocantins River in the form of the world's largest known iron ore deposit, which has a 66% iron content. The first commercially produced ore was mined in 1985 and the mine is linked to a new deep-water port at Sao Luis on the Atlantic coast by a new 800 km long railway. Although mining itself may be only a minor cause of deforestation, the associated activities, such as road and railway building and disposal of toxic waste may cause considerable environmental disruption. Some schemes have managed to avoid the worst effects by introducing a strict environmental monitoring policy. At Trombetas, north of the Amazon, extensive deposits of high-grade bauxite are worked by a consortium of Brazilian and foreign mining companies. The ore occurs quite near the surface under a ten metre overburden and can be easily worked by open-cast mining methods. This, together with on-site crushing and washing plants could have resulted in massive environmental destruction. In fact the mining company maintains an on-site ecological staff of thirty who supervise and monitor the area. Mining activity is limited to an area of about 70 ha each year, with topsoil being removed and stockpiled to be replaced later and replanted with trees grown in an on-site nursery. It is hoped that disrupted areas will have fully reverted to forest after about fifteen years.

Timber exploitation and plantation forestry

Despite the initial impression of the wealth of the Amazon being concentrated in its trees, tropical rain forest areas have, until recently, contributed relatively little to world trade in timber. The high costs of extraction due to lack of homogeneous stands, felling and transportation difficulties, labour shortages and distance from main world markets kept their share of world trade to less than 10%.

Since 1950 developed countries have increased their imports of tropical hardwoods by sixteen times. There are a number of reasons for this increase. Firstly, despite conservation methods, supplies of temperate hardwoods used in the construction industry have become depleted. Secondly, new technology in the pulp industry now allows the use of tropical hardwoods in the paper-making industry. As demand for paper and paper products from the developed world continues to soar, so increasing literacy rates in developing countries increases demand yet further.

Faced with meeting these increased demands for their trees, the temptation for hard-pressed governments in the developing world is to 'fell and sell' as quickly as possible with little regard to the environmental consequences. There are two main ways of harvesting timber: selective logging where only trees of a specified size and type are cut, and clear felling which involves the removal of the entire tree cover. Although the former method may appear to have most to commend it ecologically, studies in some forests where only 10% of trees were harvested, revealed that extraction methods seriously damaged a further 55% of the tree stock. Other critics argue that since inevitably the best trees are harvested, those remaining will be the poorer specimens and will produce poor replacements.

One attempted solution to the harvesting problems of natural forests has been the development of plantation forestry where specific species are grown together in homogeneous groups. In the Amazon such a scheme was inaugurated by the American billionaire Daniel K. Ludwig who planted quick-growing gmelina and pine trees on his 1.2 million ha Jari River plantation in order to produce cellulose. Initially, the scheme was beset with labour problems and soil erosion but now houses a population of about 25 000, mostly attracted from north-eastern Brazil. The project is now managed by a consortium of over twenty Brazilian companies and is producing cellulose, plywood and hardwood veneers indicating that plantation forestry, properly managed, makes much greater economic sense — with much less environmental impact — than the high cost extraction of individual tree species from natural forest.

All of these development projects have resulted in deforestation in varying degrees. The loss of tropical forests has become a major environmental issue creating world-wide headlines. One of the most recent and comprehensive surveys estimates that the loss is currently 5 km^2 every hour, or 210 000 km^2 each year. If this figure is correct, then almost half of today's tropical forest will have disappeared by the year 2000. Half of the species alive on earth depend on these forests and as the trees are cut down, as yet undiscovered plants and crops with possible medicinal and food supply uses, will vanish with them. One environmental organisation has claimed that if the loss of rain forests continues at present rates, 'Our generation will have presided over the greatest extinction of living things since the ecological catastrophe that wiped out the dinosaurs . . . the ecological Armageddon is already well advanced.'

9. Account for the fact that until relatively recently, the tropical rainforest areas have made relatively little contribution to world trade in timber resources. Why has demand increased in recent years?

10. Using detailed examples from Amazonia, identify and explain the reasons for current large scale deforestation. Describe the possible environmental risks of such developments.

11. Outline the traditional methods of farming in Amazonia and explain why they had relatively little impact on the forest ecosystem.

12. Referring to examples from both tropical and temperate areas, assess the suitability of forestry as an element in multi-purpose land management schemes.

7
The grasslands

It is only during the last two hundred years that the world's natural grasslands have been used by people on a large scale. In both tropical and temperate environments, temperature and precipitation patterns restricted the development of agriculture and nomadic herding and hunting continued to be the main uses of these areas until well into the nineteenth century. As the population of North America and Western Europe increased during the Industrial Revolution, the Prairies were fenced and farmed for the first time to provide cereal crops which could now be easily transported by rail and sea.

Attempts to develop permanent agriculture in the world's tropical grasslands have been more recent. Since the Second World War, population growth in many developing countries has put pressure on the savanna grasslands to meet the increasing demand for more food, as well as for foreign exchange through the production of crops for export. Although the ecosystems of tropical and temperate grasslands differ widely, both have been considerably altered by their development for commercial agriculture and their natural landscapes irreversibly changed.

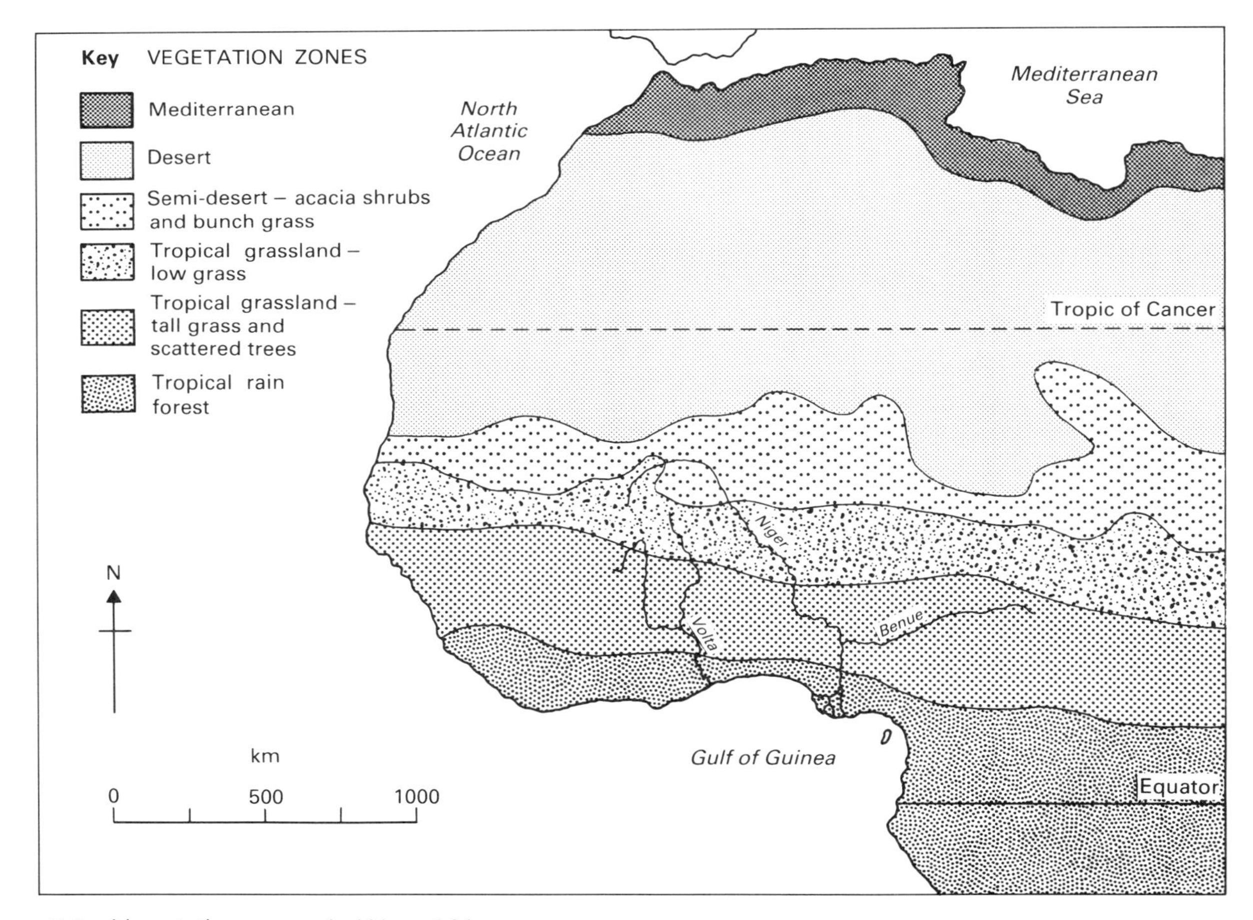

7.1 Vegetation zones in West Africa

Tropical grasslands

The main bio-climatic characteristics of tropical grasslands are outlined on p. 23. The high average temperatures and, particularly, the seasonal rainfall experienced have been responsible for the development of distinctive land-use patterns which aimed to maximise available land and water resources. The situation in the tropical grasslands of West Africa, called the **savanna** illustrates the interaction between climate and vegetation. The savanna provides an excellent example of tropical grasslands as a transitional bio-climatic zone, lying between the drier and hotter Sahara to the north, and the wetter coastal rain forests to the south (Fig. 7.1). Moving northwards from the Gulf of Guinea through Nigeria, the amount of rainfall decreases as does its reliability. Natural vegetation mirrors the seasonal pattern of rainfall changing from lush rain forest to savanna parkland with acacia and eucalyptus trees. Further north still, on the southern edges of the Sahara — the **Sahel** area, the open savanna grassland eventually gives way to short tussocky clumps of grass separated by scrubland and characterised by sagebrush and thorns (Fig. 3.4b, p. 23). Here on its northern edges, savanna vegetation is adapted to be able to withstand the alternating periods of drought and water surplus.

This transitional pattern of climate and vegetation is reflected in the land use and the problems which sometimes result from increasing population pressure on a fragile ecosystem dependent upon the maintenance of a careful balance of land and water resources.

The Fulani of Nigeria: case study

The savannas of northern Nigeria have been home to the Fulani tribes for over five hundred years. In that time, their nomadic lifestyle has adapted to the low (less than 600 mm per year) and variable rainfall principally by the development of a kind of **transhumance**, migrating south with their animals during the dry season in search of fresh pastures, and allowing the northern areas to recover without overgrazing. In the southern areas, around the Rivers Niger and Benue, permanent agriculture is possible and has increased considerably in recent years, particularly where river water is available for irrigation. Over the years a kind of symbiotic relationship had developed between the Fulani and the settled farmers:

'. . . *a visit to the rich agricultural area around the historic city of Kano in February or March at the height of the dry season, will reveal herds of animals wandering across land, which during the rainy season is covered with millet, maize, sorghum, beans and ground-nuts. Livestock graze on any vegetation they can find, depositing manure, for which the farmers may sometimes pay the herdsmen. This is the key to a highly productive farming system where fallow periods are virtually non-existent, and the same fields are cultivated year after year.*'

(J.A. Binns: People of the Six Seasons, *Geographical Magazine*, December 1984).

The pattern of movement and lifestyle which the Fulani herdsmen have developed reflects their overriding concern to provide adequate food and water for their animals. Their knowledge of local environmental conditions has evolved over many centuries but in recent years there have been signs that this traditional lifestyle is coming under threat from a variety of sources:

1. Population growth in northern Nigeria, with densities now approaching 200 people per km^2 around Kano, could have a serious effect on the relationship between the Fulani and the farmers. The herdsmen are finding that as demand for food from the city grows, their traditional source of pasture and water during the dry season, such as river valley land is now increasingly being intensively cultivated for cash crops such as vegetables. Estimates put the amount of cultivated land around Kano as already over 85% and increasingly farmers are fencing off areas to prevent damage to their crops by grazing animals.
2. The effect of the construction of several large irrigation schemes such as the Tiga Dam and the Kano River Project during the last ten years has not been entirely favourable to the Fulani. In the northern areas of Nigeria, the lack of a reliable water supply has always been a handicap to the development of permanent agriculture. Although water is now more plentiful in parts of Kano State and more intensive agriculture is developing rapidly, from the Fulani standpoint, the availability of pasture and traditional migration routes have been affected by the newly irrigated areas, thereby increasing the tension between themselves and the settled farmers.
3. Droughts during the periods 1968–73 and 1984–85, and outbreaks of disease caused by rinderpest have depleted the Fulani herds considerably.

As a result of these pressures two responses from the Fulani can be identified. The first is an increasing trend for many of them to give up their migratory pastoralism and to settle either as permanent farmers, or to seek employment in cities such as Kano. This movement has been encouraged by official government **sedenterisation** programmes. The second response is for the Fulani to have to restrict their animals to smaller areas, increasing pressure on vegetation and contributing to **desertification**.

1. Explain how agricultural land use in West Africa has traditionally reflected the limitations imposed by the rainfall pattern.
2. Why is the traditional system of nomadic pastoralism of the Fulani now coming under threat?
3. Outline the ways in which the Fulani have responded to these threats.

Desertification

Desertification or the degradation of land so that it loses its biological productivity and economic value is a worldwide problem (Fig. 7.2). Almost 35% of the world's land area is under threat of desertification and it is estimated that each year over twenty million ha of land declines in fertility to the point of yielding no net economic return and a further 6 million ha are lost to desert. According to the United Nations Environment Programme (UNEP) the annual economic loss associated with the advancing desert can be estimated at around US$6.5–7 billion. They estimate that about 700 million people live in the drylands and are faced with the risks of desertification.

Desertification in the Sahel: case study

The Sahara is the world's largest desert accounting for almost a quarter of all hot deserts in the world. In the main the Sahara is a natural, rather than a human-induced phenomenon, and its spread southwards into the countries of the Sahel (Fig. 7.3) has traditionally been blamed on natural climatic conditions. Although this does occur in a few areas, the correct term for it is **desertization**. When the United Nations Conference on Desertification (UNCOD) met in Nairobi, Kenya in 1977, it identified the four primary causes of desertification as being human-induced:

1. Overcultivation With increased population pressure, there has been a growing trend towards the cultivation of marginal lands previously used for livestock. The populations of the Sahelian countries are increasing at over 2.5% per year, but food production is only increasing at 1%. In addition to traditional cereal crops, both production of vegetables for the growing local urban markets and the extension of ground-nut cultivation for export in some of these countries has increased.

Cropping has also been more intensive with a reduction in the period of fallow — this reduces the soil's capacity to naturally replenish minerals and farmers are generally unable to afford artificial fertilizers. The cultivation of less productive and more drought-prone areas has resulted in declining crop yields and increased soil erosion.

2. Overgrazing With the extension of cropland,

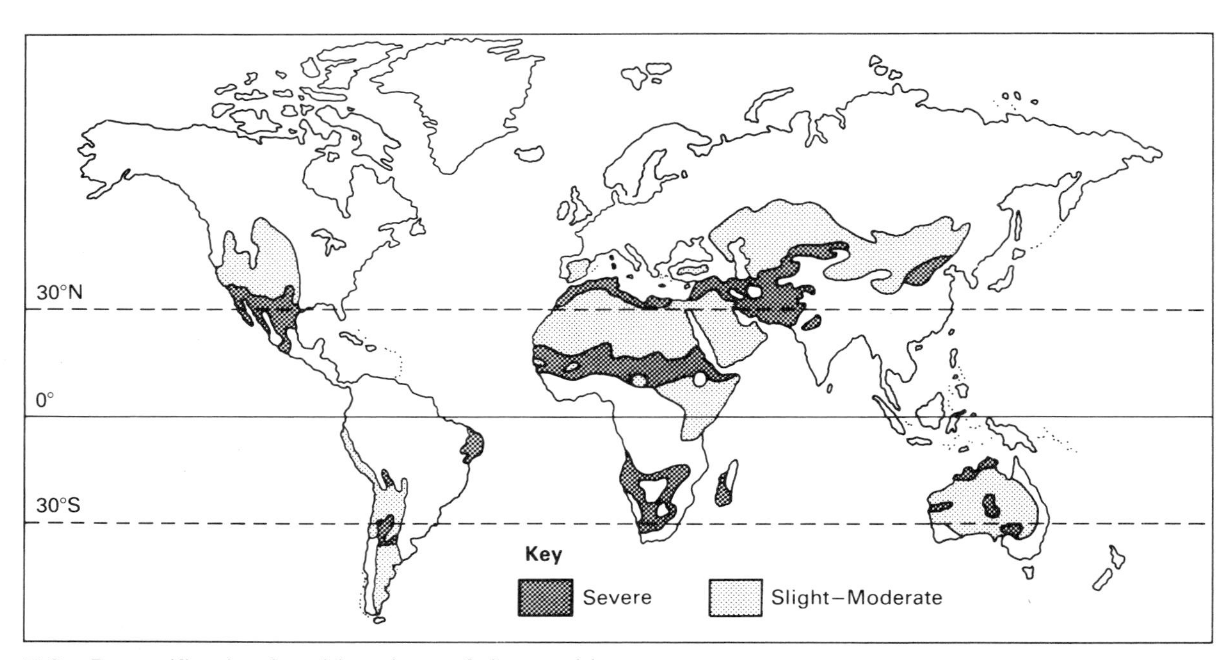

7.2 Desertification in arid regions of the world

livestock has been crowded on to smaller areas of pasture causing overgrazing. A similar problem has occurred in those countries such as Nigeria where governments have encouraged the permanent settlement or sedenterisation of previously nomadic herders such as the Fulani, whose animals now cause pressure on certain localised pastures. The situation has been exacerbated by the growing average size of herds: the traditional attitude to livestock as a source of wealth in many arid lands still prevails and as livestock density has gone up so pressure on the land has increased. This has resulted in damage to vegetation, particularly due to soil compaction by stock near waterholes. There has also been a decline in the health of livestock in affected areas resulting in a fall in milk and meat production.

3. Deforestation The United Nations Food and Agriculture Organisation (FAO) estimates that clearance of open woodlands in the arid tropics is taking place at a rate of four million ha per year, with almost 75% of this in Africa. Although the removal of trees benefits cropping and grazing in the short-term by increasing the area available for agriculture, the water table may soon fall because the land loses its capacity to absorb water, erosion of the now unprotected soil may occur and the deforested area becomes more arid. A second major pressure on the trees comes from the collection of fuelwood — about 90% of people in developing countries are dependent upon wood as their main source of fuel. Areas around many villages have become treeless deserts as wood is collected for fuel and there is an increasing demand from the growing urban population due to the high costs of alternative fuels. For example, Ouagadougou, the capital of Burkina Faso uses 100 tonnes of wood every day for cooking alone. All woodland within 40 km of the city has been felled.

4. Poor irrigation Although irrigation may seem more likely to be able to stem the cycle of desertification, where it is combined with poor drainage it can cause waterlogging and increased soil salinity and can turn land into desert. In the Sahel during the late 1970s and early 1980s some 5000 ha of newly irrigated land were being cultivated each year — but every year another 5000 ha were going out of production due to waterlogging and salinisation. Irrigation often displaces large numbers of people on to more marginal lands, which they are then forced to overcultivate, leading, inevitably to further desertification.

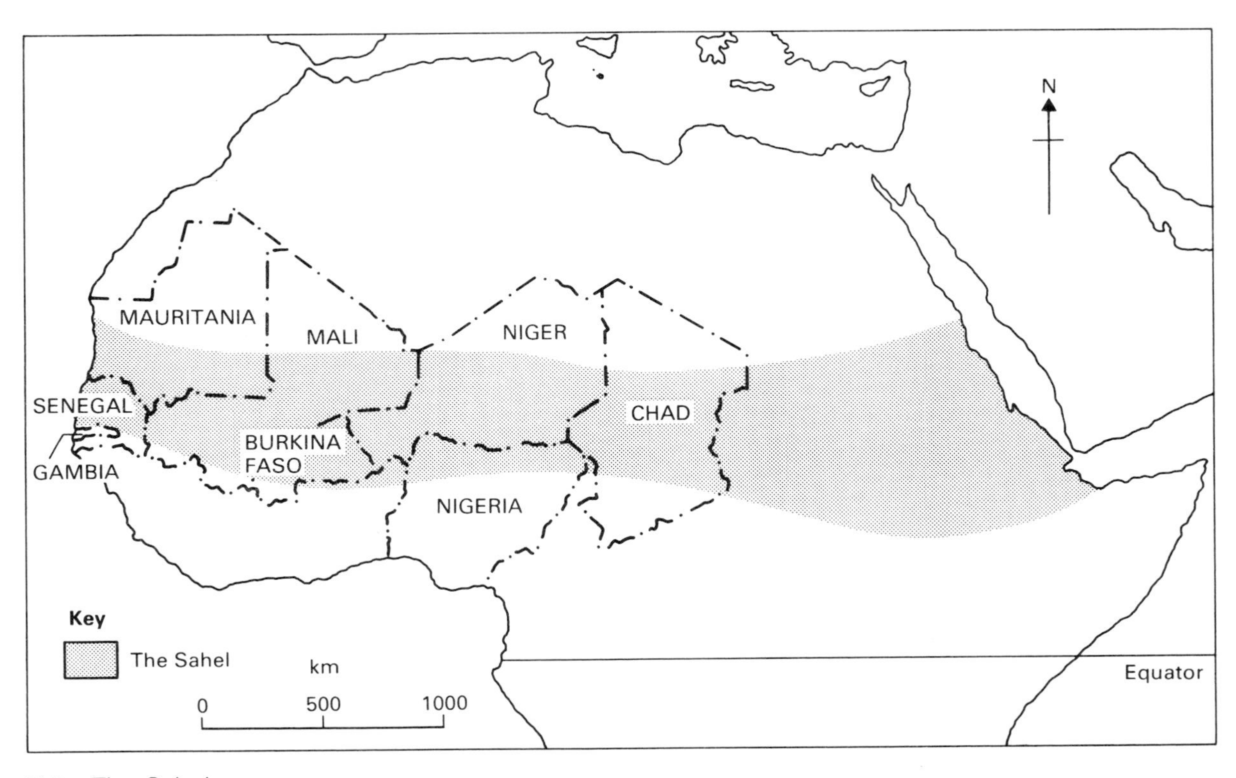

7.3 The Sahel

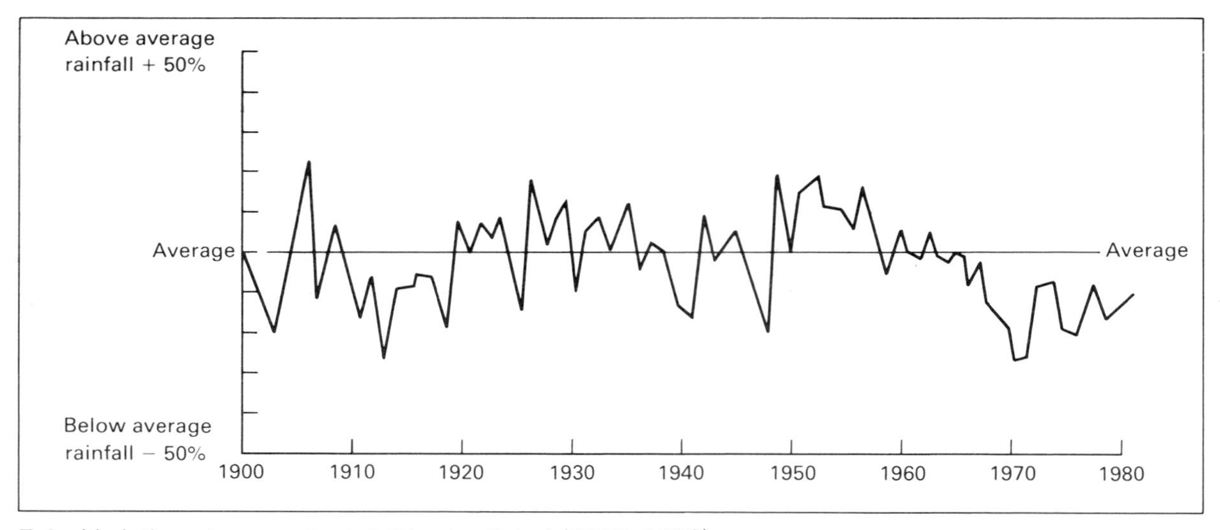

7.4 Variations in annual rainfall in the Sahel (1900–1980)

During the 1950s, the Sahel countries benefited from years of exceptionally good rains (Fig. 7.4), which encouraged the extension of rainfed crop-lands on to previously marginal pasture lands whilst increasing numbers of cattle were grazed on poor arid lands on the edges of the desert proper. Some estimates put the increases of sheep, cattle, goats and camels at 100%. In 1968 the rains came early, and were unusually heavy but had stopped by May. Crop seedlings died before the rain returned in June: there followed five years of below average rainfall and it is estimated that over 100 000 people died as a result. Amongst livestock, cattle and sheep suffered most with some herds losing 100% of stock. As the drought advanced, animals concentrated in areas of land around water-holes causing overgrazing and circles of desertified land. Many of these overgrazed areas joined together to create large expanses of denuded vegetation. In central Sudan overgrazing, soil erosion and deforestation have pushed the desert edge southwards into the savanna grasslands by about 100 km since 1970.

The underlying causes behind the problems highlighted by the drought of 1968–73 were clearly identified by UNCOD and their report aimed at the development of several transnational projects to improve stock rearing, monitor affected areas by satellite, and the establishment of massive 'green belts' north and south of the Sahara. But the fear that the same mistakes were being continued almost without change were confirmed in 1984–85 when famine swept across Africa from Senegal to Ethiopia. Once again drought had highlighted the problems of overcultivation, overgrazing, deforestation and soil erosion in leading to a decline in food production. It is important to see the causes of the 1984–85 famine in perspective. A drought is a lack of water, but does not necessarily lead to inevitable disaster. It can even be argued that prolonged droughts are almost normal phenomena in the Sahel. Whether or not a drought becomes a disaster depends on how the land has been managed before the drought. In an interview in 1985 with the American magazine *Newsweek*, the Ethiopian Relief Commissioner clearly recognised this. In analysing the problems facing his country he mentioned neither rain nor food relief: 'We have to start over again with the forestation pro-gramme. We have to start irrigation, soil and water conservation projects.'

Combatting desertification

In the Sahel there are few signs of progress against further desertification. Certainly the ambitious proposals of UNCOD such as the circum-Sahara green belt, the large-scale flooding of certain areas to increase availability of irrigation water, and the widespread evacuation of pastoralists from the affected areas are unlikely to fully materialise. The problem however, has not disappeared and there are already signs that livestock numbers, severely reduced by the droughts of 1968–73 and 1984–85, have almost recovered and are already putting renewed pressure on land and water resources. Deforestation is still taking place at an alarming rate leading to erosion, floods and further desertification, yet less than 2% of Sahel aid has been given over to reforestation projects. There is increasing pressure for farmers to grow commercial crops for export, rather than food crops and much of the available aid is being directed to the cities. Only 20–25% of Niger's annual budget goes to rural areas, a high figure for the region, yet 90% of the country's population live in the countryside. Comparative figures for Burkina Faso are 4% of the budget spent on 92% of the population.

The most hopeful developments are those which are essentially small-scale, owe much to local initiatives and aim to achieve a balance between the available environmental resources and the requirements of the human and animal populations. For example, in the early 1980s Oxfam introduced villagers in northern Burkina Faso to several cheap, simple anti-desertification techniques which had been developed by Israel in the Negev Desert. One technique involved scooping out small 'bowls' in the soil thereby creating 'micro-catchment areas' for water which was directed on to the base of tree seedlings which Oxfam hoped to grow for fuel wood. The villagers adopted the techniques successfully, but also introduced different varieties of trees for fodder, fruits and nuts. The villagers then decided that food crops were even more important than trees and began to adapt the water-focusing technique for growing millet.

Other projects have included those developed by the Six S's organisation (*Se Servir de la Saison Séche en Savanne et au Sahel*: Making use of the Dry Season in the Savanna and the Sahel), which by 1985 had organised 700 village groups in Burkina Faso, 300 in Senegal and 200 in Togo. The organisation runs 'schools' to teach village leaders new techniques for which it can also provide limited financial assistance. These Six S's village groups have undertaken small irrigation and drainage projects and undertaken erosion control and reforestation schemes. They have developed nurseries for fruit trees and built new village grain storage facilities. Their efforts are based on two slogans: 'Development without destruction' and 'The peasant: what he is, what he knows, how he lives and what he needs'.

If desertification in the Sahel is to be halted, and the process eventually reversed then it is more likely to be the result of the work of non-governmental organisations (NGOs) such as Six S's and Oxfam who direct their efforts at the village and people level. There are signs that the success of this 'grass-roots' approach is now even recognised by the United Nations. In analysing the failures of its own UNCOD Plan of Action in 1984, a UN report admitted that:

'In some respects, NGOs have been the most effective agencies in the campaign against desertification. Dozens of them around the world have become involved, above all in field projects such as tree planting, and soil and water conservation . . . Their high record of success is related to the small scale and local direction of their projects and the requirements for local community participätion as well as their flexibility in operation and their ability to learn from other mistakes. The dominance of field activities gives these actions an impact out of all proportion to the money invested.'

4. Referring to Fig. 7.2 describe the distribution of areas of severe desertification.

5. Briefly explain the difference between the processes of desertification and desertisation.

6. Using Figs. 7.3 and 7.4 explain why the Sahel area is particularly vulnerable to both types of desert advance.

7. Identify and explain in detail the primary causes of desertification in the Sahel.

8. Assess the relative success of schemes designed to combat desertification, in the Sahelian countries, contrasting in particular large and small-scale projects.

Temperate grasslands

In much the same way that the tropical grasslands of West Africa can be seen as an intermediate biome between the hot deserts and tropical rain forests, so the cooler, temperate grasslands can also be regarded as a transitional zone. Usually, the precipitation varying between 250–750 mm per year is too low to yield enough water for forest, but is above the level experienced by desert areas. Temperatures range from well below zero in winter to summer maxima up to 20°C. Grasses dominated the natural vegetation which also included a wide variety of other plants which contributed to the formation of a deep, fertile humus (p. 27). In areas such as the North American Prairies and the Steppes of USSR this complex ecosystem has been greatly simplified by the introduction of extensive farming involving the replacement of the natural vegetation by perhaps only one cereal crop. The problems associated with monoculture in the grasslands have already been discussed and today these areas are more carefully managed with crop and livestock rotations and fertilizer applications, supplying a large proportion of the world's food.

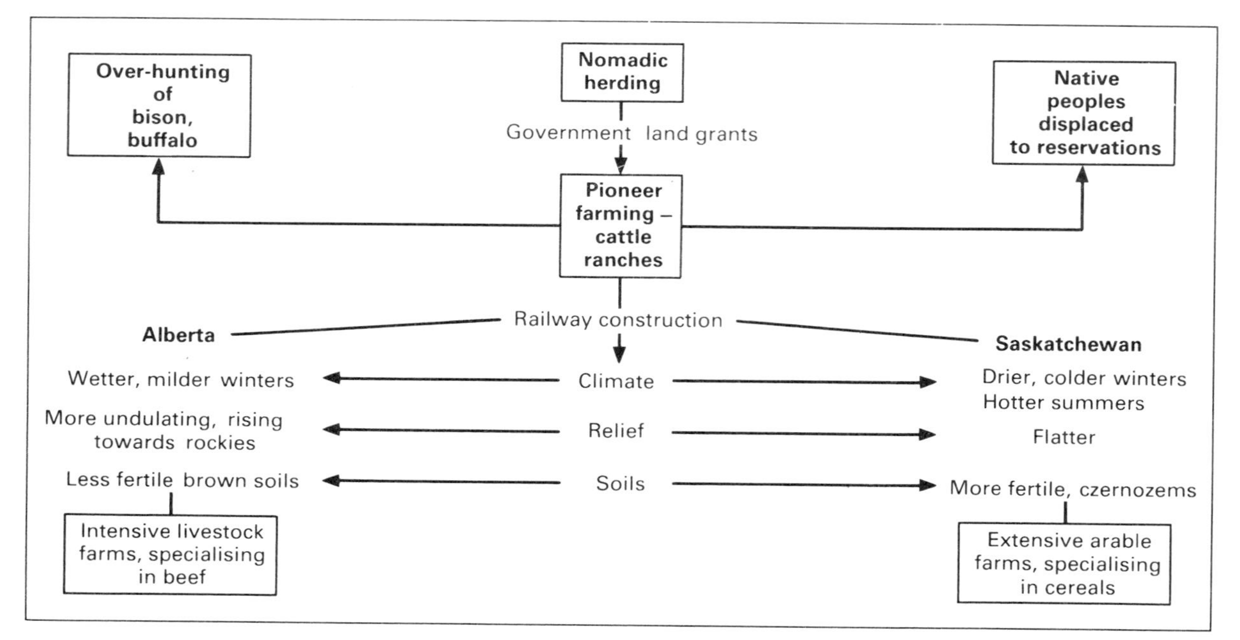

7.5 Farming changes in the western Canadian Prairies

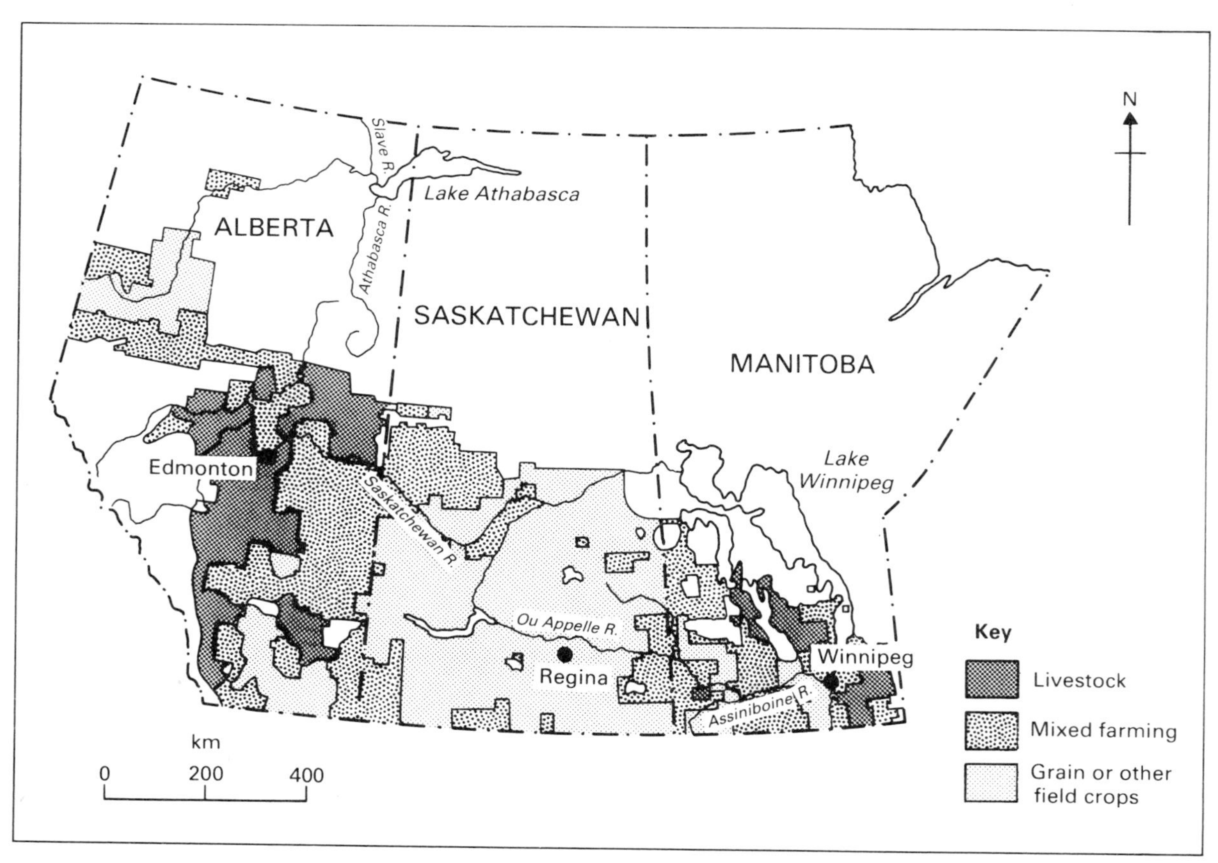

7.6 Prairie region main farming types

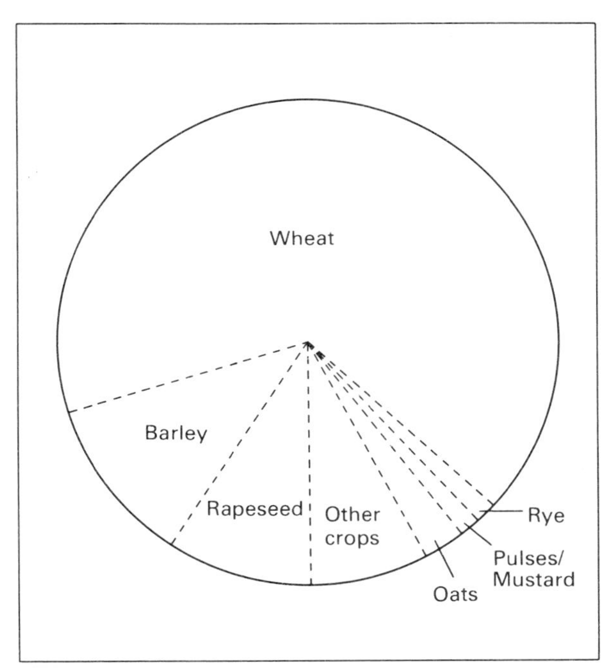

7.7 Principal field crops, Saskatchewan

The Canadian Prairies — farming in Saskatchewan: case study

The natural open grassland vegetation of the Prairie Provinces of Canada — Alberta, Saskatchewan and Manitoba (Fig. 7.5) — was the home of bison, hunted by the plains Assinboine Indians. Although new settlers pushed west during the nineteenth century, progress was very slow and by 1812 had only reached the Red River Valley near Winnipeg. In 1872 the Canadian government offered free land to new colonists, usually in blocks of 64 ha — but the main impetus came with the extension of the Canadian Pacific Railway across the Prairies in 1882–85. Most farms were initially confined to a zone of 15 km on either side of the railway, giving farmers access to the transport facilities for their animals and crops. Although most of the early farmers were cattlemen (see Fig. 7.6), there was some arable farming and the first shipment of prairie grain was made in 1877 to Great Britain. As demand for cereals increased, particularly from Europe and the developing cities of the east, large areas of rangeland were ploughed up and planted with wheat. Today, 75% of Canada's farmland lies in the three Prairie Provinces and there is a continuing westward shift of the productive farmland base as physically and economically marginal land in eastern Canada is abandoned. Saskatchewan alone has over half of Canada's prime farmland, divided amongst 70 000 farms which average 400 ha in size. The increased dominance of the Prairies can be attributed to a number of reasons, exemplified by the Province of Saskatchewan.

Fig. 7.7 shows the proportions of field crops grown in Saskatchewan in 1985. Although there has been some diversification in recent years to peas, mustard, and sunflowers, the dominance of cereal crops, particularly wheat, is clear.

Climatic advantages

The long, cold winters are accompanied by hard frosts which help to break up the soils. In the spring, snow melt in the west of the province is hastened by the Chinook, a warm wind descending from the Rockies and the frost-free season ranges between 105–135 days, allowing the growth of spring wheat which requires about 100 days without frost. Summer temperatures average 15°C and are accompanied by light rainfall during the growing season. Daylight hours are long during the summer months, often up to 16 hours which encourages the rapid growth and development of the crop as well as assisting harvesting in the early autumn.

Soils

In the central, wetter areas of Saskatchewan, where grain farming is mainly concentrated, fertile, black earth soils or czernozems occur (p. 35). These mineral and humus-rich soils are ideal for cereal cultivation, but need to be carefully managed. Overcultivation, wheat monoculture and poor soil conservation up to the 1930s resulted in loss of topsoil. In recent years most of Saskatchewan's wheat crop has been seeded on land which has been **summer fallowed** the previous year. Summerfallow is land kept out of production and tilled only to prevent weed growth. The purpose is to conserve soil moisture and allow the build-up of plant nutrients in the soil. This practice does, however, take land out of production for a year and the trend towards crop diversification mentioned earlier allows land to be used as part of a planned crop rotation. Another system, called **zero tillage**, is also used and involves planting the crop directly into unploughed land, thus keeping soil disturbance to a minimum and retaining soil moisture. The increased use of fertilizers also allows land to be more intensively used, either by using cattle grazing as part of the rotation pattern for manure, or by applying artificial fertilizers.

Landscape

Although there is a gently rising gradient across the Prairies from east to west, the relief generally is very flat broken only by occasional ridges and river valleys. The following extract from Hugh MacLennan's *The Colour of Canada* describes the nature of the Prairie:

'*Often when you drive along a prairie road, running straight to the horizon, you have the illusion that something is the matter with your car — that it has become stationary. When you fly across it after dark, it seems dotted with fireflies — lights from the barns and windows of farmhouses with occasionally a blaze of light that is a city or town.*'

These level plains have greatly assisted farming mechanisation, an important factor in Saskatchewan which has a relatively low population density and where the period since 1945 has seen a decline in farm population. At harvest time the picture of teams of combine harvesters working across the monotonously flat landscape has become almost a symbol of modern **extensive** Prairie farming (Fig. 7.8). Although Prairie farming is highly mechanised, the historical background to 19th century land allocation meant that virtually all farms were family controlled. Until recently Saskatchewan was losing population — mainly to the cities — and there was concern that family farmers would be replaced by national or multinational 'agribusiness' operations, similar to those found in areas such as California. In order to prevent this, the Saskatchewan government has created a 'land-bank', buying farms from farmers who wished to retire and leasing them to young farmers with an option to buy. They are supported by an extensive technical development and advice programme working on crop strains, pest and weed control sponsored by the province, and a comprehensive crop insurance service protects farmers from loss through natural disasters.

Co-operatives

Most modern Saskatchewan farms have high levels of capital investment in equipment, and some is shared between farmers who are members of co-operatives. These groups are particularly important to farmers for grain marketing and one such, the Saskatchewan Wheat Pool, is one of the world's largest co-operative wheat handling organisations. The Pool owns the computerised grain elevators (Fig. 7.9) located at railheads throughout the prairies, to which farmers deliver their grain, before transportation mainly for export. Although the cost of moving the grain is met by the farmers, freight rates are controlled by statute and kept low. All wheat produced by the co-operatives or 'pools' is bought by the Canadian

7.8 Saskatchewan, Canadian Prairies

7.9 Grain elevator, Saskatchewan

Wheat Board which controls marketing at home and abroad. The main export routes used by the Saskatchewan Pool are shown on Fig. 7.10. Although traditionally, Western Europe provided the main market for Prairie wheat, over half of Canadian grain exports now go to developing countries, and other new markets include Japan and China, supplied from the ports at Vancouver and Prince Rupert.

Improved crops and techniques

The northern Prairies can almost be regarded as an agricultural 'frontier' with more land being brought into cultivation as further advances have been made in more rapidly-maturing and frost-resistant crop varieties. Some strains of wheat now require only a ninety day frost-free growing season and so the cultivated area has moved

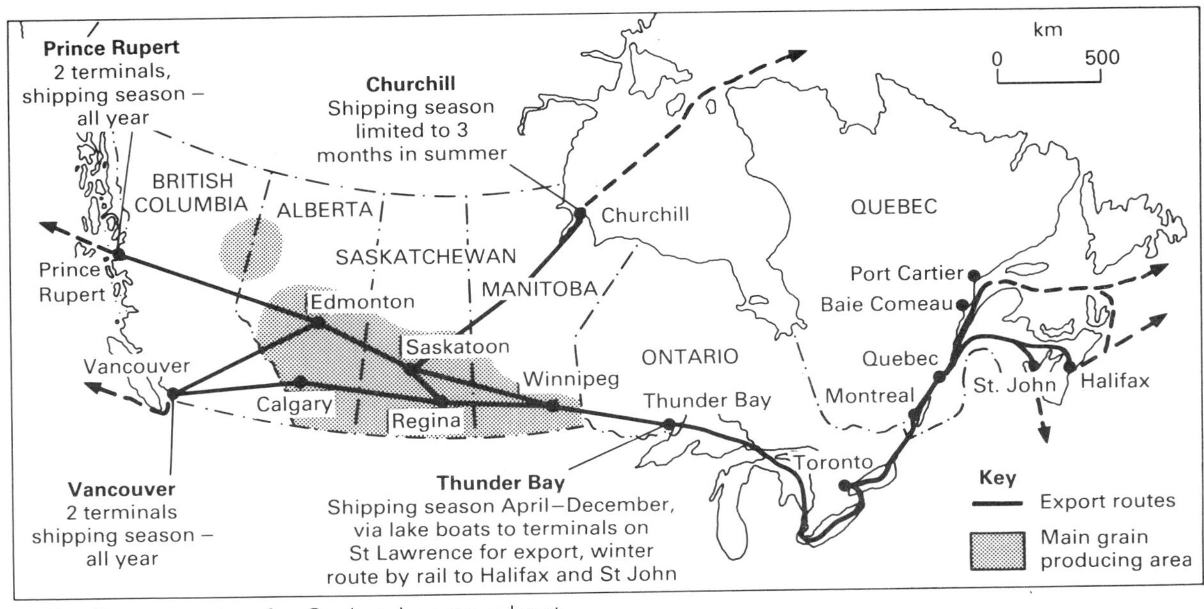

7.10 Export routes for Saskatchewan wheat

northwards. In order to convert bushland into improved farmland, inexpensive clearance and tillage have been made possible by new types of farm equipment for which government grants may be available to help with costs. Although rainfall is lower in this northern area, irrigation has been developed, particularly from the Saskatchewan River and its tributaries which reach their flood peaks after the spring thaw. Thus, most irrigation water is available when needed for plant germination. Throughout Saskatchewan, soil erosion has been greatly reduced by conservation techniques such as the planting of shelter belts of trees to act as windbreaks across the flat landscape, and strip farming involving the planting of wheat in 100 metre wide strips with fallow land, or moisture-retaining crops, in between.

During the depression years of the 1930s, Saskatchewan was Canada's poorest province. The dependence on monoculture of wheat and poor farming techniques led to declining farm incomes, and rural depopulation was so great that a provincial joke asked, 'Will the last person to leave please put out the lights?' Fifty years later, the Cinderella province appears to have inherited the earth. With slow but sustained population growth, improved and mechanised farming, and a growing mining industry based on oil, natural gas and uranium, economists estimate that during the 1990s it will have the greatest sustained growth rate of all the Canadian provinces.

9. With reference to Fig. 7.5, describe and explain the changing pattern of farming on the Canadian Prairies during the 19th century.

10. Referring to factors such as climate, soils and relief, explain the dominance of wheat cultivation in Saskatchewan.

11. Describe the changes in farming techniques and crop developments which have taken place in Saskatchewan in recent years and outline their effects on the farming community.

12. Describe and explain the differing export routes for Saskatchewan wheat, taking into account any recent changes in markets.

8
The deserts

Of all of the world's **biomes**, it is probably the deserts or those areas receiving an annual precipitation of less than 250 mm which offer fewest attractions for permanent human occupation. Deserts in total cover almost 25% of the earth's land surface (semi-desert 13%, hot desert 8% and tundra 2%) but their extreme temperatures, low rainfall and scant vegetation make these areas unsuited to most crops and therefore permanent settlement. Traditionally the human response to these hostile environments was the evolution of a nomadic pastoralism such as practised by the Bedouin of the Arabian Peninsula, or the hunting lifestyle of the North American Inuit with relatively few permanent settlements. More recently however, as the world's more accessible mineral reserves have been worked out, there has been increased development in areas such as northwest Australia, the Arabian Peninsula, northern Canada and Alaska which has had considerable impact on the landscape and the indigenous population.

1. Describe the main physical difficulties which desert environments present for permanent human settlement.
2. Briefly outline how native peoples have traditionally adapted to the environments of both hot and cold deserts.

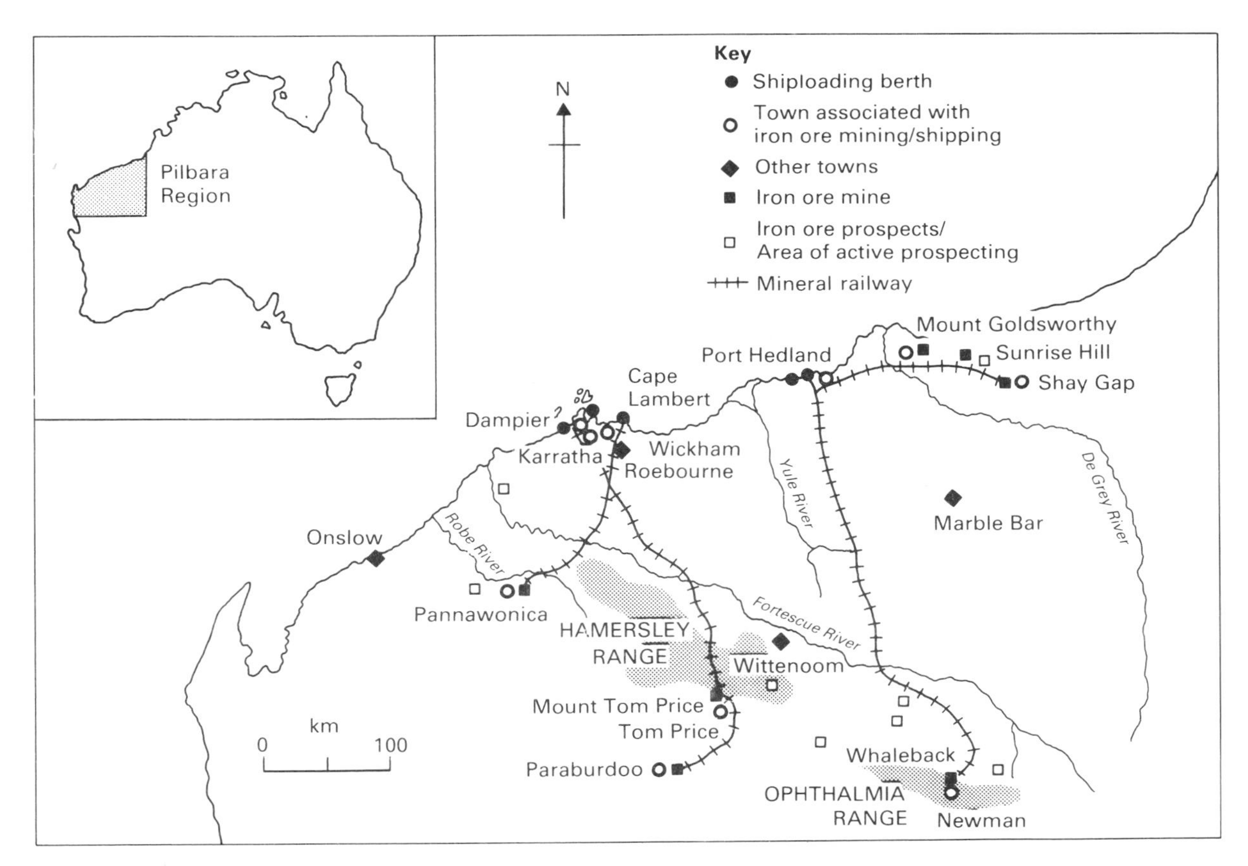

8.1 Iron ore mining, Pilbara, Australia

Iron ore mining in north-west Australia: case study

The environment

The Pilbara semi-desert region of north-west Australia (Fig. 8.1), is one of the hottest areas in the world with Marble Bar, south of Port-Hedland, having recorded temperatures of over 32°C on 151 consecutive days. Inland, around the modern mining settlements near the Tropic of Capricorn, desert conditions prevail with annual rainfall below 250 mm increasing towards the coast. Until recently the area had attracted few settlers and in 1960 the region's population was less than 3000 — mostly concentrated in a few coastal settlements. The interior is a huge dissected plateau of pre-Cambrian rocks broken by ridges of higher ground, rising to Mount Bruce at 1226 m. The plateau surface is gashed with several spectacular gorges — Australia's Grand Canyon country, which attracted a few adventurous tourists.

Resource discovery

Initial surveys and mineral prospecting first took place in the area over a century ago. Although extensive deposits of iron ore were discovered at that time, no full evaluation or resource development took place until the 1960s for a number of reasons:

1. The area was several thousand kilometres from the main centres of population and industry located in the south-east of Australia, and communications with other areas were very poor.
2. The desert and semi-desert environment presented many problems.
3. Iron ore deposits in the Middleback Range of South Australia could easily meet the demand from the small-scale Australian iron and steel industry and were, in any case, much closer to the markets.
4. During the 1930s the Australian government had imposed an embargo on all mineral exports in order to conserve national reserves.

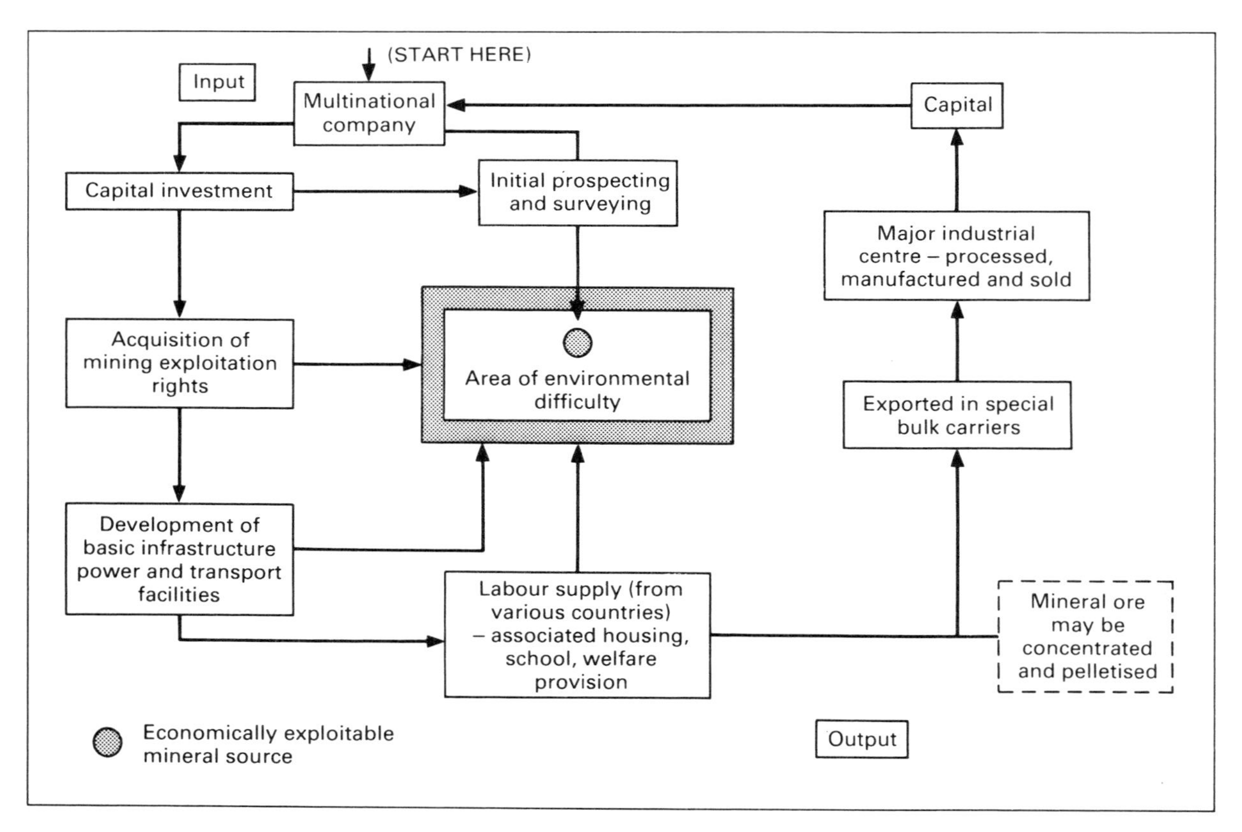

8.2 Input and output model of mining development in an area of environmental difficulty

Resource evaluation and development

Following the Second World War an extensive evaluation of Australia's mineral wealth was undertaken by the Geology and Mines Department which estimated the iron ore reserves of the Pilbara to be 100 000 million tonnes mostly with a metal content exceeding 60% and described by one geologist as being '. . . like trying to calculate how much air there is!' Even this evaluation did not guarantee the development of the iron ore. Production and transport required large expenditures, and despite the presence of the substantial reserves, even multinational companies were initially wary of investing in such a remote and difficult region. The first incentive came in 1960 with the lifting of the embargo on Australian mineral exports but the crucial factor which finally encouraged development was market demand. The phenomenal post-war growth of Japanese industry, particularly in metal-related products with high output rates provided this market since the Japanese iron and steel industry requires to import over 90% of its iron ore requirements. Japan is still a long way from Western Australia, however, but ore movement was facilitated by the 1960s revolution in bulk sea transport. This meant that huge bulk-ore carriers of up to 250 000 tonnes were able to move large quantities of mineral ore by sea, thus dramatically reducing transport costs.

Mining developments

Four major companies, Hamersley Iron, Mount Newman Mining, Goldsworth and Cliffs Robe River invested vast sums of money to develop the ore reserves. Due to the high capital investment, much of the finance was provided from overseas with multinational corporations having majority holdings in the mining companies (see Fig. 8.2).

The ores occur at or close to the surface, often in ridges which allow open-cast mining using modern extraction techniques. Primary and secondary ore treatment takes place on site before loading on to rail wagons which make up trains of 180 trucks. New rail links were constructed between the mines and deep-water coastal terminals at Dampier and Port Hedland where ore can be stockpiled and pelletised to 90% purity before export in bulk carriers.

The new mining communities

Apart from the cost of developing the mines, railways and port facilities, the companies have also had to create a human environment for living and working in desert conditions which have few attractions for settlement. Wages are considerably higher than the national average for mine-workers to attract people to an area 1600 km away from Perth, the nearest city. New towns 'mushroomed' to house the miners and their families in air-conditioned houses surrounded by trees and landscaped areas. Provision has been made for sporting and recreational facilities as well as schools, hospitals, libraries and improved communications. All goods in the company-controlled shops are brought in from the south and prices are held at Perth levels.

Yet there are problems. The workforce is almost entirely male with over forty different nationalities attracted by the high wage levels. Few stay for very long, contributing to a generally unsettled atmosphere. Despite the development of alternative markets during the 1980s, the area has been called 'a Japanese quarry' with over 80% of ore from the region still destined for Japan. This over-dependence on one mineral and one market could cause problems in the future, a price slump or a drop in demand could see the settlements become mining 'ghost towns'. Although the mining companies contribute substantial amounts in mining royalties to the state government, there is no doubt that multinational interests in the two mining companies have taken large profits out of Australia altogether. Nevertheless, despite this creaming off of both profits and natural resources, there is no doubt that few other developments could have opened up this corner of the Australian desert outback or contributed so much to the country's export trade in such a short time span.

3. Why did development of the Pilbara's iron ore reserves not take place before the 1960s?

4. Using Figs. 8.1 and 8.2 write an account of the exploitation of iron ore reserves in the Pilbara. You should refer to the stages of development shown in the model and discuss the problems encountered by the mining companies and the infrastructural developments necessary to develop the resource.

Agricultural developments in Saudi Arabia: case study

The discovery and development of oil reserves in the Arabian peninsula (Fig. 8.3) has had a profound effect on the development of many Arab states, some were transformed from traditional nomadic Bedouin cultures into countries with some of the world's highest per capita incomes and rates of car ownership. The extent of their influence on world trade became apparent in 1973 when the OPEC states doubled oil prices and caused serious problems for oil-importing nations. That action demonstrated to these countries the importance of developing a self-sufficient energy policy to make them less reliant on oil imports. From the point of view of the Arab states, their reliance on imported food, necessary because of their desert climate, is no less emotive. Some states, notably Saudi Arabia and the United Arab Emirates have invested large sums from their oil revenues in recent years in transforming desert environments into productive farms with the aid of modern irrigation techniques.

In Saudia Arabia, increased food production was an important element in the state's Third Development Plan from 1980–85. As well as reducing dependency on imported food, the plan aimed to provide more jobs in rural areas and make maximum use of the kingdom's limited water resources by irrigation schemes. In 1975 some 150 000 ha of land were cultivated, with about 25% irrigated and the remainder rain-fed. By the end of the Third Plan in 1985, the area under cultivation had increased to 2 000 000 ha, the majority of which used modern irrigation techniques such as the central pivot system (over 15 000 now in operation) and were often sponsored by government investment. Research was carried out by the Arid Zones Institute of the University of Arizona in USA and much of the technology employed in Saudi Arabia was developed in Arizona. In order to encourage farmers to grow certain crops, notably cereals such as wheat and barley, a price guarantee system has been in operation. Increased production of wheat exemplifies the rapid expansion of cultivation: from less than 4000 tonnes in 1978 to an amazing 1.3 million tonnes in 1984 which even allowed a surplus for export. Despite this huge increase in production, there has not been an equivalent increase in jobs for the rural Saudi population. Much of the new farmland is controlled by a few multi-national 'agri-businesses' which employ European and American farm managers and labour from the Far East — particularly from the Philippines. Farms employ the most modern cultivation methods and labour inputs are anyway fairly low.

Much of the water for irrigation has come from the kingdom's extensive system of **aquifers** and the existence of these traditional sources of water has influenced the extent of the latest agricultural developments. It is possible to identify a 'fertile crescent' of cultivated land from Tabuk in the north-west, through Hail and near the capital at Riyadh to Wadi ad Dawasir (Fig. 8.3). Inevitably, the increased pumping of water in this area has led to increased water salinity and low pressure and now wells have to be drilled down to 1500 m

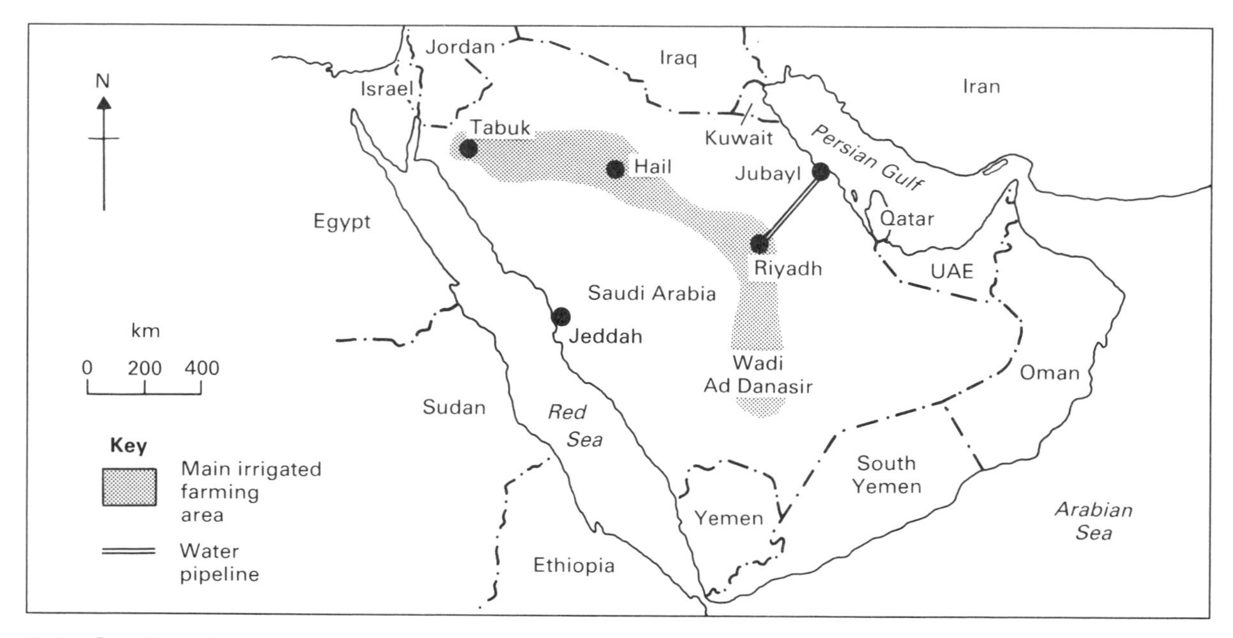

8.3 Saudi Arabia

to overcome these problems. In coastal areas where overpumping has occurred there has been sea-water infiltration of the aquifers resulting in even greater salinity. A new water pipeline has been built from a massive desalination plant on the coast at Jubayl to the capital at Riyadh and as well as meeting domestic demand, some will also be used for agriculture in the central area. Availability of irrigation water for farmers around urban centres such as Jeddah has encouraged the cultivation of more specialist crops e.g. fruit and vegetables, and there has even been considerable expansion of dairy farming and poultry production. Saudi Arabia is now almost self-sufficient in chickens, eggs and milk and this sector, together with horticulture, is likely to see most expansion in the future providing that water can be made available at an economic cost.

8.4 Greening the desert, Jeddah, Saudi Arabia. Particularly around cities in the desert countries of the Middle East, attempts have been made to extend intensive agriculture into semi-desert fringes by the use of irrigation. These intensive projects have made extensive use of the high levels of insolation in desert areas to counteract other environmental difficulties. In particular the types of crops grown are ones people in the West would identify as market garden crops such as fruits, vegetables and flowers which need to be produced fresh.

5. What are the advantages to Saudi Arabia of the development of irrigated food crops?

6. Identify and explain the problems which have been encountered in the expansion of irrigation.

The Tundra

The Canadian Northlands — the environment and the native people: case study

Talk of the 'Northlands' and the Inuit still evokes images of romantic landscapes and of native people living a traditional and isolated lifestyle in harmony with their natural environment. It is also increasingly outdated:

'The North scarcely lives up to its romantic image. It is a harsh, hard place . . . Its bleak beauty occasionally hypnotises Southerners . . . but most Canadians have never been north of the sixtieth parallel . . . and have not the slightest wish to do so.'

(John Young, writing in *The Times*)

Although Canada is the world's second largest country in area, the majority of the Canadian population is located in the cities in the south near the US border and the north is still regarded as 'frontier' country to some extent. The Canadian northlands (here defined as all land north of latitude 60°N, in the Yukon and North West Territories), cover a vast land area of 3776 million km^2 or 40% of the entire country, yet the total population in 1981 was around 68 500 people, concentrated in relatively few communities (Fig. 8.5). The environment is harsh, ranging from true tundra (tree-less plain) to the northern edges of the taiga where the permafrost is discontinuous and vegetation consists of pine trees and muskeg or swamp. As economic activity has increased, particularly in relation to mineral developments, the pace of change in the region has gathered momentum, and there has been a growing concern over the effects on the lives of the native peoples and on the region's sensitive ecosystem.

Rather less than half of the region's population can be classified as being of native ancestry with the Inuit being the largest group. Before contact with white society, these people had evolved traditional hunting economies based on the harvesting of fish and mammals for food and fur and their lifestyles illustrated a technical mastery of the harsh tundra environment. Settlements were scattered and often the Inuit groups moved around using dog teams and sledges in search of food, building igloos as temporary homes in winter and living in tents whilst hunting during the summer. The Hudson's Bay Company began trading in the area as early as the 17th century. Furs were traded for guns, metal knives and animal traps which obviously had far-reaching implications for the native economy but caused little social disruption until the 1930s when fur prices collapsed and the Inuit were no longer able to afford the white technology on which they had come to rely. Further social disruption came with the Christian missionary movement during the 1920s and 1930s which brought churches and schools into the northlands. Despite good intentions, it is now recognised that the missions created considerable disruption in Inuit family life and traditional culture. Children were separated from their parents to attend mission-run schools where the use of native languages was often banned. Recently the NWT government has attempted to reverse this policy of 'cultural assimilation' and instead younger children are now taught entirely in Inuktitut, with English introduced gradually in the senior years with up to 40 percent of class time spent on native cultural education.

Even greater social change came with the arrival of the Distant Early Warning (DEW) radar bases and military stations of the 1950s and more recently, with mineral explorations. Already mines north of 60°N in Canada produce all of the country's tungsten, 44% of its lead, 26% of its zinc, 20% of its silver, 13% of its gold and considerable amounts of cadmium and copper. Mining in the area faces the obvious difficulties of environment and distance from market and is heavily dependent upon high metal prices. Nevertheless, the area includes the world's most northerly metal mine, opened in 1982 on Little Cornwallis Island, where lead and zinc are produced.

Oil and gas exploration began on a large scale in the 1970s and several highly promising areas have been identified, particularly in the Mackenzie Delta, Beaufort Sea and the Sverdrup Basin (Fig. 8.5), which may eventually account for up to a quarter of Canada's oil and a third of the national gas reserves.

In an effort to protect Arctic ecosystems, several areas have been designated as National

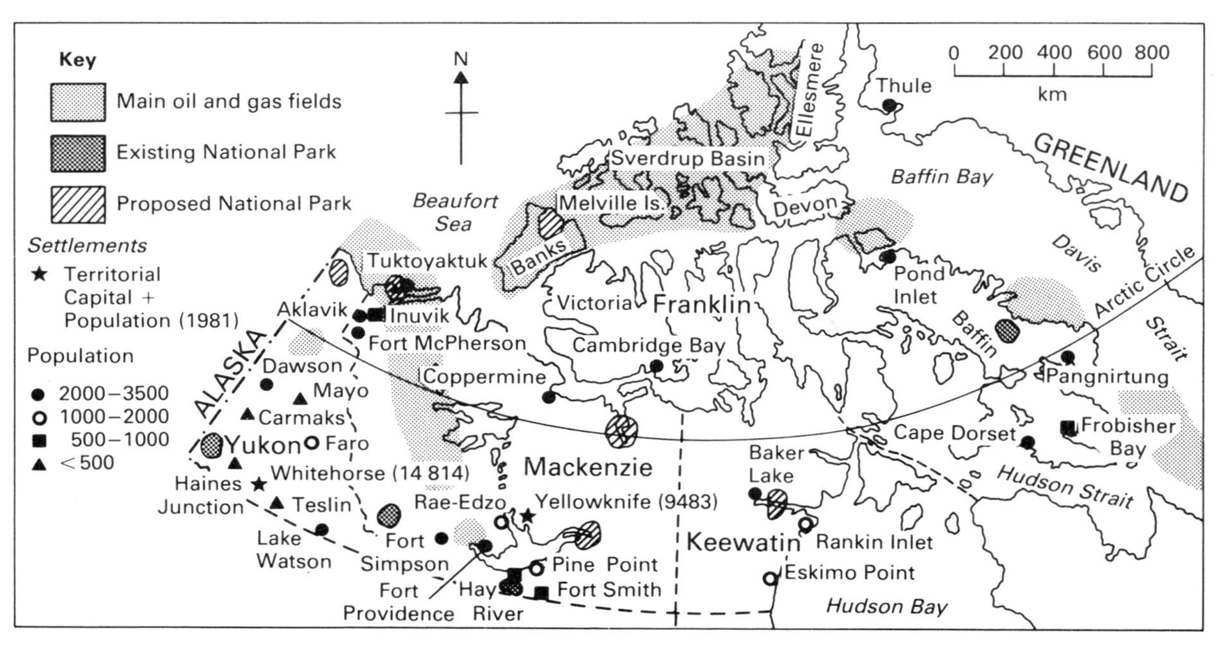

8.5 The Canadian Northlands

Parks (Fig. 8.5) where land-use is strictly controlled, exploration for non-renewable resources is banned, and hunting and fishing may only be undertaken by native peoples.

High wages have attracted native workers to the mining developments in large numbers but often work is limited to unskilled construction jobs and may last for only a short period. Mineral developments in the northlands are always likely to be economically tenuous, their operation dependent on world prices. Oil exploration in the Beaufort Sea was halted in 1986 due to the collapse of oil prices, with drilling rigs laid up at Tuktoyaktuk, and workers paid off until more favourable economic conditions return.

The imposition of a monetary-based economy however has caused lasting disruption to the traditional way of life. As an increasingly urban lifestyle spread into the non-urban northern culture, traditional skills of igloo-building, fishing and hunting were not being learnt to the extent that the Canadian government then had to introduce unemployment benefit for some groups of native workers. More recently almost 50 Inuit-run co-operative organisations have been established. As well as returning to the exploitation of fish, seals, polar bears and caribou, traditional handicrafts such as soapstone carvings and paintings are encouraged with the co-operative arranging marketing in the south. The co-ops employ about 350 people in NWT alone, almost all of whom are native people. One such organisation is based at Baker Lake (Fig. 8.5), Canada's only inland Inuit settlement. Located 320 km upstream on a tributary of Hudson Bay, and 480 km north of the tree-line, Baker Lake has a population of some 900 Inuit. Despite the expansion of wage employment into the local economy, in the form of the co-operative, government services and some tourism, less than half of the local school leavers find employment. Some combine the modern urban lifestyle with their traditional hunting economy. A recent visitor to the settlement describes the lifestyle of today's Inuit:

Pirjuaq and Tulurialik each live there with their respective families in a three-bedroomed house, equipped with modern kitchen appliances, telephones, televisions and VCRs. Tulurialik often sits in his living room playing his electric guitar. For men that grew up in igloos and skin tents, this represents a massive change in lifestyle. It is not, however, uncommon to see a large hunk of raw caribou on the kitchen floor amid this setting. The food is the same, but the social fabric of the community it nourishes is much changed.'

(David Pelly, *The Geographical Magazine*, March 1987)

Government policy is now to encourage self-help amongst the native population and some of the Inuit now demand a self-governing homeland (Nunavut, literally 'Our Land') based on their distinctive language and culture. As hydrocarbon exploration has expanded in the northlands there has been increased tension between the Inuit and the Canadian government over territorial rights over traditional hunting grounds. In 1982 the Canadian government agreed to the division of NWT into two regions, roughly divided by the tree line, above which the population was 75% Inuit, virtually assuring them of some form of self-government. Whether government is controlled from Ottawa, Yellowknife or locally, the social problems of the region remain acute. Widespread alcoholism is now a major contributor to death rates amongst the Inuit. General health problems are more acute than elsewhere in Canada as the whites brought new diseases such as tuberculosis and measles, for which the native population had no natural resistance. The native infant mortality rate is about three times higher than that for non-native infants and suicide rates are high throughout the native population. The attempts at cultural assimilation clearly have had far reaching consequences.

7. Identify the main stages in contact between the native peoples of the Canadian tundra and outside influences.

8. In what ways have these contacts been:
   a) beneficial
   b) detrimental

   to the traditional lifestyle of the Inuit?

9. Explain why 'mineral developments in the northlands are always likely to be economically tenuous'.

Alaska North Slope oil and the Trans-Alaska Pipeline: case study

In 1968 the largest known deposits of oil and gas in North America were discovered below North Slope, overlooking Prudhoe Bay in Alaska. Despite the size of the deposits, the tundra environment and remoteness from the major US markets delayed the development of the reserves until 1973. The massive increase in world oil prices instigated by the Arab-dominated cartel OPEC in 1978, gave new impetus to resolving the problems posed for the extraction and transportation of Alaskan oil. The price increases made it now worthwhile for the oil companies to consider the economics more seriously, and the US government and people had been made painfully aware of the consequences of relying too heavily on imported oil, particularly from the Middle East.

Problems of oil extraction

1. The severely cold climate of the area where temperatures may only rise above freezing for 2–3 months each year, blizzard conditions are common, and wind-chill reduces temperatures still further. Human flesh freezes on exposure to the air and drilling and communications equipment have to be expensively adapted. High wages are paid with workers commuting by air from Fairbanks and Anchorage and working 12-hour shifts for eight days out of every fourteen. The workforce, currently over 2000, spend their non-working hours in a climatically-controlled environment with many sporting and recreational facilities provided.
2. Due to the presence of underlying **permafrost**, all buildings and drilling work are set on 2 m thick wooden 'rafts' which 'float' during the summer thaw and insulate the permafrost from the heat produced by buildings during the winter, preventing thawing which would cause foundations to collapse.
3. During the 9-month long winter the area can be in continual darkness making work both difficult and dangerous. Expensive arc-lights and flares are used continuously to allow work to proceed around the clock.
4. The area is extremely remote and transportation of labour and supplies is both difficult and expensive. Although a new road link with the Trans-Alaskan highway has been completed, it is frequently impassable due to weather conditions. Heavy freight is brought in by sea-route, which is open for only six weeks each year, and personnel, foodstuffs and urgent spares are brought in by air.
5. As in the North Sea, there are a number of wells spread throughout the producing area. Collection is by a network of local pipelines which pump the oil and gas to central gathering points for transportation.

Once the oil had been extracted from below this inhospitable environment, the problem of transporting it to the main markets in the rest of the USA had to be resolved. Initially, the Alaskan government undertook a feasibility study of moving the oil by tanker, through the pack-ice of the North West Passage, to the east coast of the USA. The route proved to be impractical for a number of reasons. Vast quantities of oil would have to be stored for much of the year, followed by a race of tankers during the 6-week open season of the Beaufort Sea. The route was also found to be slow (speeds by the new ice-breaker the SS Manhattan were reduced to 150 m per hour), as well as dangerous. It was also unlikely that the Canadian government would sanction the passage of vast quantities of oil through its environmentally sensitive tundra areas due to the considerable risks of spillage. The solution came with the construction of a 1300 km long pipeline southwards to the ice-free Pacific port of Valdez, although this was to face considerable problems of construction as well as massive opposition from

8.6 Trans-Alaska oil pipeline

a number of environmental groups. These ranged from international organisations such as Friends of the Earth to local groups of native Inuit who saw the pipeline as a threat to their traditional way of life. In the event, the 1973 OPEC oil crisis ensured that the economic case for the construction of the pipeline would outweigh the conservation arguments although, as Fig. 8.7 indicates, the pipeline has been built to stringent safety standards to minimise the risk of oil spillage and limit its environmental impact as far as is possible with a structure of its size.

10. Explain why the 1973 OPEC oil-price increase proved to be crucial for the development of Alaskan oil?

11. Identify and explain the main problems of oil extraction on North Slope.

12. Discuss the economic arguments for and the conservation arguments against the construction of the Trans-Alaska Oil Pipeline.

13. Outline the main difficulties faced by the pipeline builders and describe the methods used to overcome these problems.

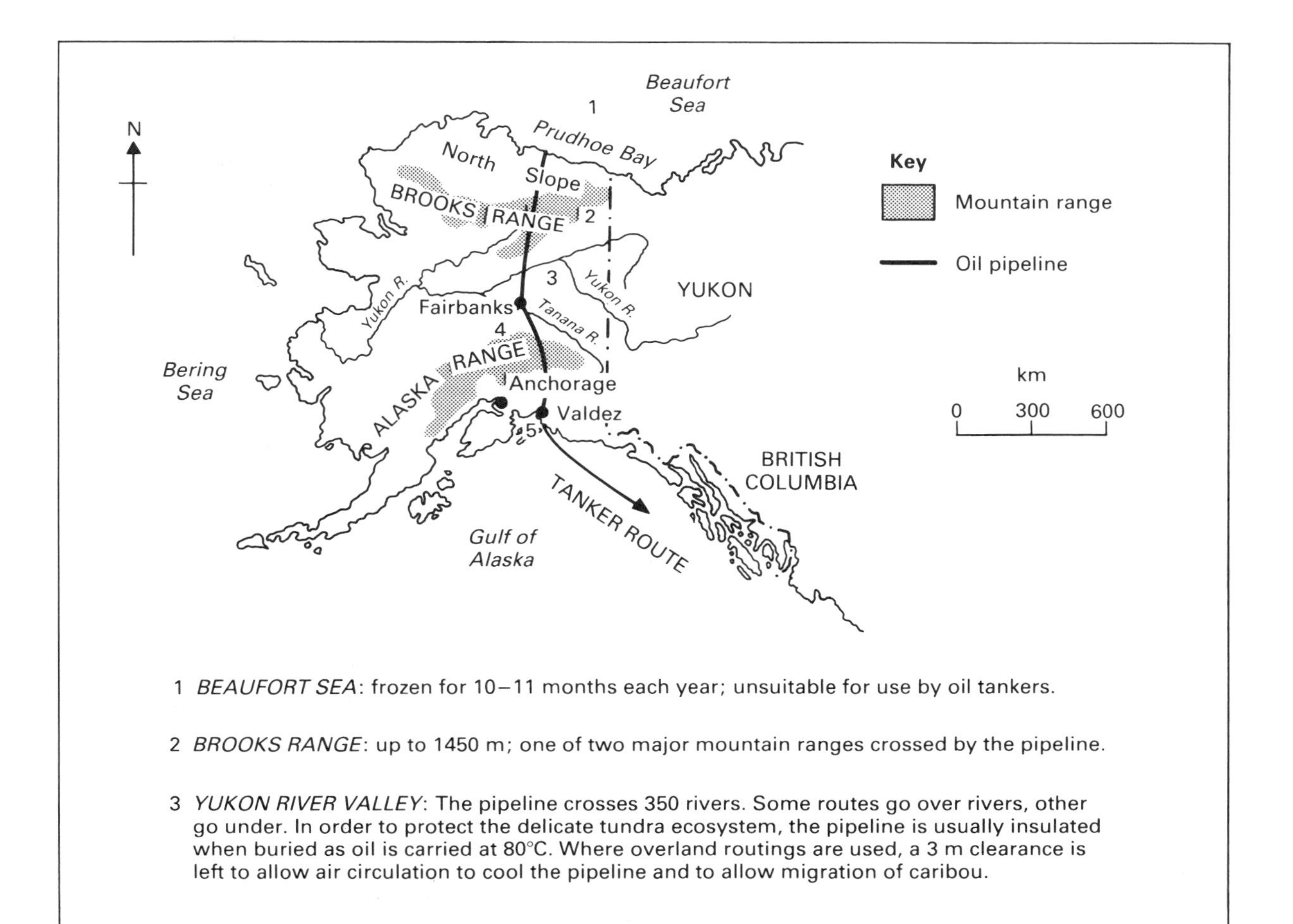

1 *BEAUFORT SEA*: frozen for 10–11 months each year; unsuitable for use by oil tankers.

2 *BROOKS RANGE*: up to 1450 m; one of two major mountain ranges crossed by the pipeline.

3 *YUKON RIVER VALLEY*: The pipeline crosses 350 rivers. Some routes go over rivers, other go under. In order to protect the delicate tundra ecosystem, the pipeline is usually insulated when buried as oil is carried at 80°C. Where overland routings are used, a 3 m clearance is left to allow air circulation to cool the pipeline and to allow migration of caribou.

4 *CENTRAL ALASKA*: is an active earthquake zone. The pipeline is built in a zig-zag pattern in this area to allow both vertical and horizontal movement without fracture. Pumping stations are located along the route to allow a closedown in an emergency.

5 *VALDEZ:* ice-free Pacific port; extensive oil storage facilities to allow transhipment of oil to Seattle and California.

8.7 The Alaskan oil pipeline route

9

Mediterranean and monsoon lands

Mediterranean lands

Despite their name, areas which experience the warm, temperate 'Mediterranean' climate, are spread throughout the world (Fig. 3.7a, p. 26), although most are located on the western margins of continental land masses. The bioclimatic characteristics of these areas have already been discussed (see chapter 3) and have considerably influenced human use of their land and water resources. Whilst their warm year-round temperatures encourage cultivation of a wide range of crops, and have resulted in the development of extensive tourist-related industries, water supply shortages resulting from the summer drought can cause severe problems for farmers and holiday resorts alike.

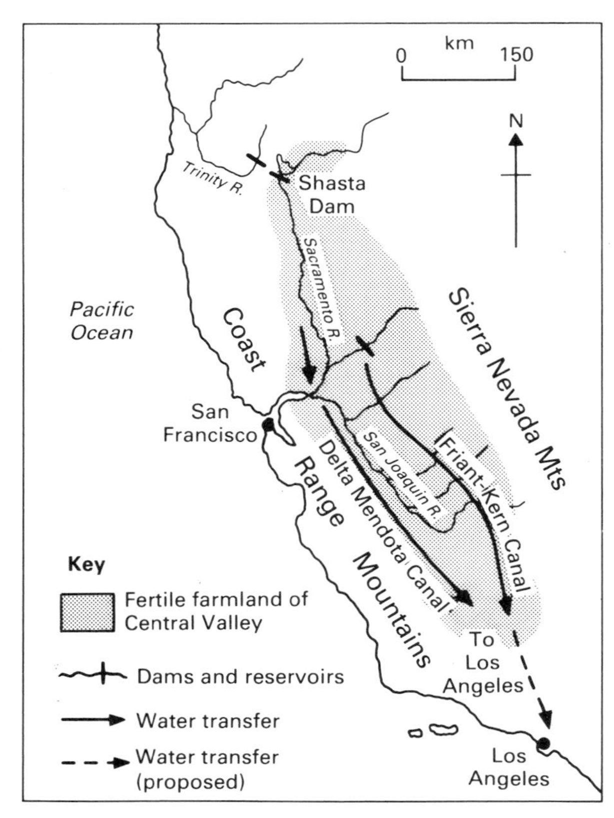

9.1 The Californian Water Transfer scheme

The San Joaquin Valley: case study

The San Joaquin Valley, running north-west by south-east between the Coastal Range Mountains and the Sierra Nevada in California (Fig. 9.1), has the combination of both fertile soils and a long growing season and has become one of the world's most productive agricultural areas. The southern San Joaquin is natural desert whereas in its natural state the northern part of the valley was semi-arid grassland with some small open oak woodland. Rainfall increases from minimum 130 mm in the south to 350 mm further north with almost all falling in winter: like other Mediterranean areas, southern California's climate is characterised by summer drought. The key to the transformation of this area into one of the world's most efficient and prosperous farming areas has been the development of **irrigation**.

The intensive cultivation of crops began in this area during the second half of the 19th century with dryland wheat farming, but with increasing demand from the State's rapidly growing cities around the beginning of this century, farmers near the eastern edge of the Valley started growing a wider variety of crops using irrigation water from streams flowing from the Sierra Nevada. Other farmers, whose land was further away from surface water supplies, began tapping ground-water sources. With the aid of advancing technology — the centrifugal pump and deep-well turbines, use of ground-water increased rapidly with farmers competing to dig deeper wells and draw more water. The race to build wells eased in the 1920s and 30s when dams and large reservoirs were built to control the flow of water from the Sierra Nevada and provided valley farmers with a guaranteed annual water supply for irrigation. By the Second World War an aqueduct had been built to carry water from the north of the San Joaquin to the drier, southern part of the valley. At the same time, the further extensive development of tubewells tapped ground-water supplies and supplemented surface water sources. By the mid 1980s, about 40% of the irrigation water used in the valley came from tubewells, 40% from controlled surface streams in the San Joaquin Basin, and the remaining 20% from canals bringing in supplies from outside the basin.

The warm temperatures experienced in the valley farms, and the level surface makes the laying out of irrigation and drainage systems relatively straightforward. As might be expected, capital investment is high and the most modern irrigation techniques are used, mostly involving sprinklers which may be either the mobile side-wheel-roll system (Fig. 9.2) or the centre-pivot system which is capable of irrigating up to 200 ha. These sprinkler systems have several advantages over traditional surface irrigation systems:

1. Salinisation is reduced because the volume of water applied is less.
2. Moderate to steep slopes can be irrigated efficiently.
3. They can be used effectively with tubewells and centre-pivot systems are usually integrated with ground-water supplies.
4. Irrigation of very porous soils is much more efficient because much less water is lost through evaporation in delivery to the plant.

There are, however, some disadvantages:

1. High winds can hamper the even distribution of water, and occasionally even damage sprinkler equipment.
2. Some crops, especially citrus fruits, may be adversely affected by the constant wetting of their foliage. This may lead to the development of bacterial and fungal diseases, and salts in the irrigation water can be absorbed through their leaves.

Following successful experiments in Israel, some Californian farms have introduced drip or trickle irrigation techniques which involves pumping water through long, narrow plastic tubes and discharging it through tiny uniformly spaced holes along the tubes which are placed on, or just below, the surface. These systems have been able to overcome some of the problems of other methods referred to above:

1. They use little water and need lower pressure to operate than sprinklers.
2. They are extremely efficient, losing no water through seepage and very little to evaporation unlike sprinklers or surface systems.
3. They are not affected by strong winds.
4. They can also effectively deliver liquid fertilizers and pesticides mixed with the irrigation water.

Farmers have to weigh these against some disadvantages:

1. So far, the drip systems have proved most cost-effective with tree and bush type row crops such as vines and citrus fruits. They are unlikely to be as efficient as sprinklers with field crops such as grain or rice because many hundreds of metres of tubing would be needed for each hectare.

9.2 Mobile side wheel roll irrigators, USA

2. A major problem concerns the clogging of the discharge holes. This leads to non-uniform water discharge and wetting of the soil leading in turn to salinity and water deficits. Efficient filtering is necessary to avoid clogging, but the systems require frequent flushing and careful monitoring.

Today, the valley's 1.9 million ha of irrigated cropland and 1.5 million ha of grassland produce an annual agricultural output valued at around US $5 billion consisting mainly of cotton, fruit, cereals, tomatoes, alfalfa, nuts, beef, wool and dairy products. California now produces well over half of all US fruit and vegetables and productivity continues to increase with farms merging to create agri-businesses, often controlled by large business corporations for which farming may be only one of a number of interests. *The Financial Times* quotes the effects of such companies in creating a farming system which owes more to manufacturing than traditional agriculture:

'*Using Tenneco chemicals, and Tenneco oil in Tenneco tractors, Tenneco farmers till Tenneco land to grow Tenneco vegetables for Tenneco processing plants that use Tenneco food preservatives in Tenneco packages for the trip in a Tenneco lorry to ultimate sale under a Tenneco brand name.*'

Although it may seem as if conditions in the valley are ideal for this kind of commercial farming and that the only problem — lack of adequate water supplies — has been satisfactorily resolved, in fact the area is now having to come to terms with several potentially serious problems resulting from its water use policies.

Cost The irrigated land is making an important contribution to US food supply and contributes considerably to California's gross domestic product, but economists have argued that irrigation agriculture is not the most cost-effective use of water in a state where shortages can also affect industrial production. Per 5000 litres of water drawn per day, it is estimated that manufacturing industry provides 4 times as much personal income, and creates 60 times as much product value than farming. Farmers do not have to bid for water against other potential users, if they did, and an economic rate prevailed, most would go out of business and their farms revert to scrubland.

Salinisation This is threatening to become a major problem. Although as yet only a few hundred hectares of land have gone out of crop production, it is estimated that some 162 000 ha now have high saline water tables and their crop yields have declined by an average of 10% as a result. Unless salinisation is controlled, by the year 2080, 445 000 ha of cropland, or a quarter of the present total, will be unusable. One solution is already in use in about 40% of the San Joaquin's cropland which has sub-surface drainage consisting of permeable pipes laid 2–3 m below the surface. These pipes drain off salts leached from the soil and prevent water tables from rising further. Even here, the disposing of the saline waste water poses a growing problem. Currently, this is led into evaporation ponds, but these are gradually leading to an accumulation of salt water. To use the natural drainage facilities of the San Joaquin River offers no solution either since in the delta area further north, the river water is extensively used for both agricultural and domestic supplies.

The US Bureau of Reclamation has recommended a 470 km master drain, following the natural drainage course along the entire length of the Valley. This drain would deposit the saline water into a tidal inlet of the Pacific Ocean beyond the San Joaquin Delta. The cost of this project would be at least US $350 million (1984 price) and if farmers who used the drain had to contribute towards its capital and operating costs, it would cost them about $150 per ha. Apart from cost implications, there are also reservations over the environmental consequences of such a project. The likely effects of the disposal of a large volume of saline water, loaded with pesticides and fertilizers on the tidal inlet and its linked fresh-water delta ecosystem is being assessed, but it is unlikely to be beneficial!

Evaporation Although the high average temperatures are vital for crop growth, they result in high evaporation rates which can lead to salt encrustation. It is estimated that less than one-third of irrigation water in some parts of the San Joaquin Valley actually reaches the crops due to high evaporation rates.

Depletion of resources The importance of the contribution of ground-water via tubewells has already been mentioned; in some parts of the Valley land has been taken out of cultivation because so much water has been removed by boreholes that the water-table has fallen and they have dried up.

Dam siltation Several of the Sierra Nevada dams are beginning to show signs of filling with river-borne silt. Although attempts are being made to reduce this by more effective soil conservation around reservoirs, storage capacity in some has been severely reduced. No cost-effective method of removing silt has so far been found. In many cases the cost of removal exceeds the cost of building the dam.

1. Explain why irrigation is necessary for farming in the Californian Central Valley and describe the benefits which it has brought to the area.

2. Describe the changing methods of irrigation used during the 20th century and outline the advantages and disadvantages of each system.

3. Water-use policies in the Central Valley are coming under increasing criticism. Describe the main problems which have resulted from attempts to control water resources in the area and suggest steps which might be taken to minimise these problems.

The Costa del Sol: case study

The Mediterranean coast of Spain has established itself as a popular holiday destination for millions of Britons each year, and in 1984 almost 750 000 bookings were made for the Costa del Sol, the area stretching from Estepona in the west, through Malaga to Almeria in the east (Fig. 9.3). The area has capitalized on its superb climate and year-round sunshine, with former humble fishing villages such as Torremolinos, Marbella and Fuengirola developing since the mid 1950s into world-famous resorts attracting visitors from throughout northern Europe. To a certain extent however, the coastal fringe with its high-rise hotels, apartment blocks and fashionable shopping centres is no more than a facade (Fig. 9.4) hiding the gulf which has arisen between these 'recreation towns' and the backward rural hinterland lying in the sierras and beyond. In recent years the Spanish government has attempted to spread the effects of tourism more widely by encouraging visitors, particularly from other parts of Spain, to visit the attractive villages further inland publicising for example the 'Ruta de los pueblos blancos' (the route of the white villages) through the villages of Andalusia.

Farming along the Mediterranean coast of Spain has traditionally faced many problems, some natural, others historical. The very climate and rugged interior landscape which are so attractive for tourists cause considerable problems for farmers. Inland the dry limestone sierras where soils are often dried out by the high rates of evapotranspiration have often been badly eroded through overgrazing and timber cutting. Summer water shortages in particular led to a concentration on drought-resistant crops and an almost monocultural specialisation in olives and vines. These crops were also ideal for the owners of **latifundios** or large estates which dominated agricultural land holdings. Productivity remained low because the latifundios were able to take advantage of the cheap labour force from the landless peasantry and this also tended to discourage mechanisation and farming improvements, leaving these large estates undercapitalized.

The period since the mid 1950s has seen massive changes in both the agricultural landscape and farming systems. With increasing demand for land along the coastal fringe, many enterprising farmers have sold out to the developers, or to large-scale farming entrepreneurs, the new style latifundistas whose 'company farms' are beginning to resemble those in California and practice the most modern agricultural techniques. Summer water shortages are less common nowadays and Spain has completed one dam every month since 1939 including several in the sierras near Malaga controlling the flow of the Casarabonela and its tributaries allowing the extension of intensive farming into a large area to the west of the town. This huerta, or irrigated farmland, much of which is under plastic greenhouses, is able to produce crops such as citrus fruit and early ripening produce such as green beans, tomatoes and avocados at least a month ahead of most of the rest of Spain and there has also been some diversification into new crops such as sugar-cane and bananas. With further extension of marketing co-operatives and associated packing and processing industries, the south coast of Spain could become Europe's main supplier of early fruit and vegetables — taking full advantage of the country's entry into the European Community in 1986. Apart from this, the possibilities of demand

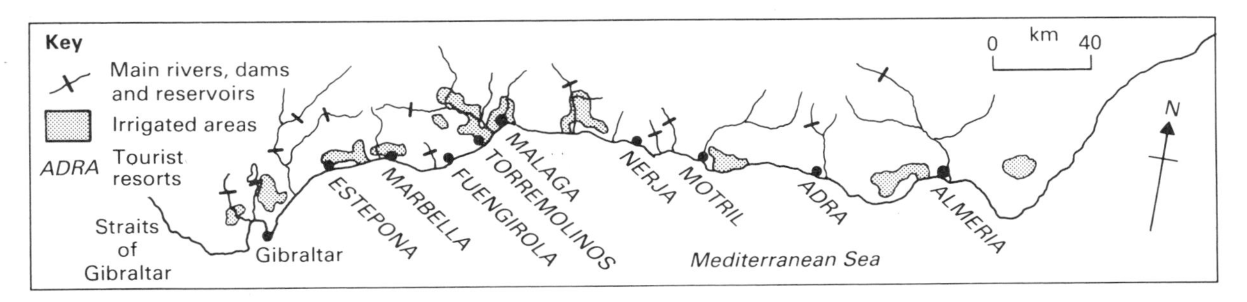

9.3 Costa del Sol : main tourist centres and irrigated areas

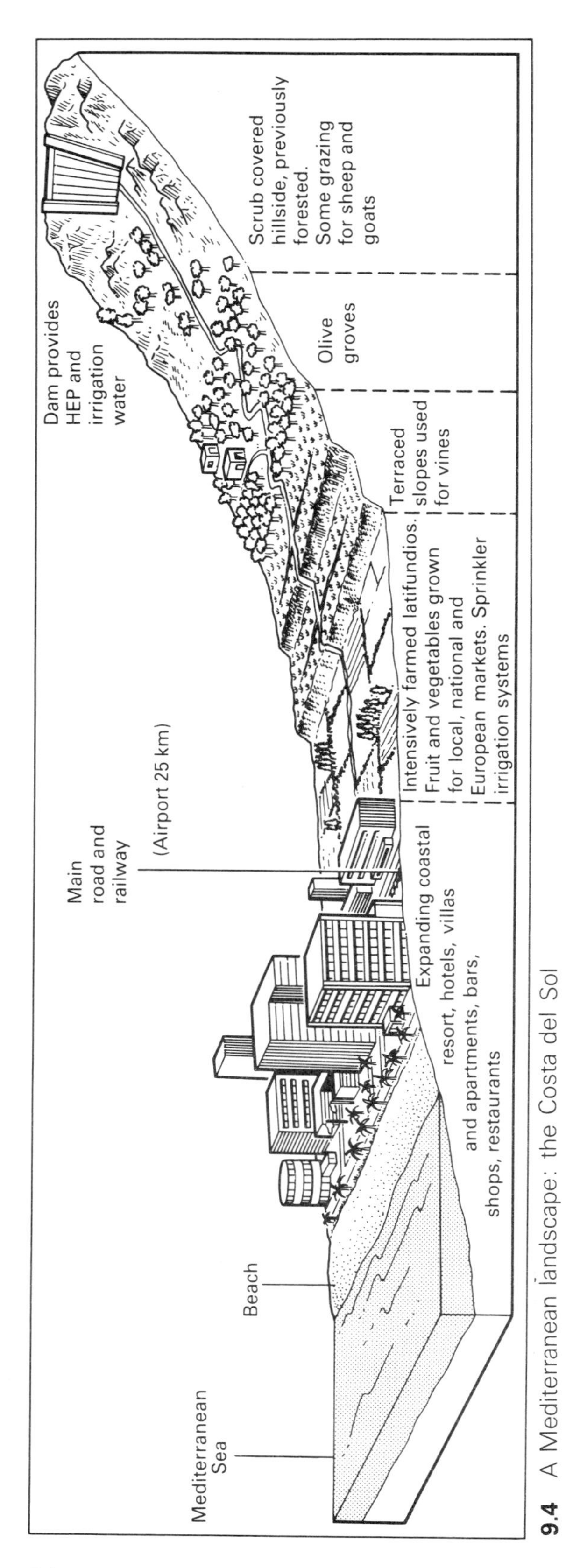

9.4 A Mediterranean landscape: the Costa del Sol

offered from Spain's own increasingly prosperous and urbanized population and the millions of tourists attracted to the area each year are likely to result in further intensification of agriculture in the area through further investment in irrigation and in modern, high-tech cultivation techniques.

4. Describe and explain how traditional farming systems in areas such as the Costa del Sol were adapted to the environmental difficulties of the area.

5. Suggest how modern farming techniques have been able to overcome many of these difficulties and suggest why the area is likely to see a considerable intensification of agricultural production in future years.

Monsoon Lands

As in the Mediterranean lands, for most of the monsoon lands temperatures are ideal for farming virtually all year round. The primary influence on farming is the availability of water, and as a result human interference with the natural water cycle has been necessary in order to overcome the problems of the monsoon climate described in greater detail in Fig. 3.6b, p. 25. Principally these problems concern the alternation of a wet and dry season and the relative unreliability of rainfall in certain areas. The solution has been the adoption of water storage and irrigation systems which regulate the flow of water throughout the year. In addition, crop specialisation reflects best use of scarce water resources to produce maximum output. Southern Asia's agriculture is dominated by production of cereal crops, in particular rice and wheat, both of which make considerable demands on water resources. Throughout the Indian sub-continent, as production of cereals has increased to meet the food requirements of a growing population, irrigation has played a major part in the gradual **extensification** of agriculture. The seasonal rainfall distribution has always played a major role in influencing agricultural development and until the widespread development of modern irrigation systems, the **kharif** or rainy season crop dominated. Even as recently as the 1960s it is estimated that 2.5 times as much water was available for crops during the wetter summer months compared with the rabi or dry winter season. During the last twenty years, however, the growing use of irrigation, particularly on the Indus Plains of northern India and Pakistan has encouraged an expansion of rabi season cropping, and particularly of new High Yield Varieties (HYVs).

Pakistan. Agricultural development on the Indus plains: case study

This cross-border region between India and Pakistan has shown that human interference with the hydrological cycle in order to make maximum use of scarce water resources dates back at least 2000 years. Traditional systems in eastern and southern India used tanks — created by small dams built across water courses. Larger farms each had their own tank which could irrigate an area of up to 30 ha and these systems are still in wide use in southern India, Sri Lanka and Thailand. In northern India and Pakistan, wells were more common but they extracted very little water, were very labour-intensive and seldom irrigated more than a couple of hectares.

Large-scale irrigation systems are, of course, more recent but a permanent dam across the Ravi, a tributary of the Indus was constructed as early as 1859. This made it possible to divert water from the river for irrigation purposes on the Indus plains. Today about 75% of the natural flow of the Indus and its tributaries is used for irrigation (Figs 9.5a and b) and in Pakistan alone the irrigation network consists of some 62 230 km of water channels. Some 17 barrages along the river system divert irrigation water throughout the year to 9 million ha of cropland and a further 4.5 million ha receive seasonal supplies, usually from mid-April to mid-October. The political partition of India and Pakistan in 1947 cut across the Indus drainage basin and the pre-existing irrigation system and posed a major threat to the water supplies for an important agricultural area in the east of Pakistan (Fig. 9.5a). Two of the world's largest dams, at Mangla on the River Jhelum (completed 1968) and at Tarbela on the Indus (1982), were constructed by Pakistan along with associated link canals (Fig. 9.5b) to ensure that irrigation water still reached the agricultural areas in the east of the country after the rivers Ravi, Beas and Sutlej were allocated to India under the 1960 Indus Waters Treaty. Both of these dams have already been severely affected by deforestation around the upper reaches of the rivers in Kashmir. The Mangla Dam receives so much silt and debris from the watershed of the Jhelum that its operational life has been halved from one hundred to only fifty years. At Tarbela, on the upper reaches of the Indus, the largest dam in the world will be silted up within forty years.

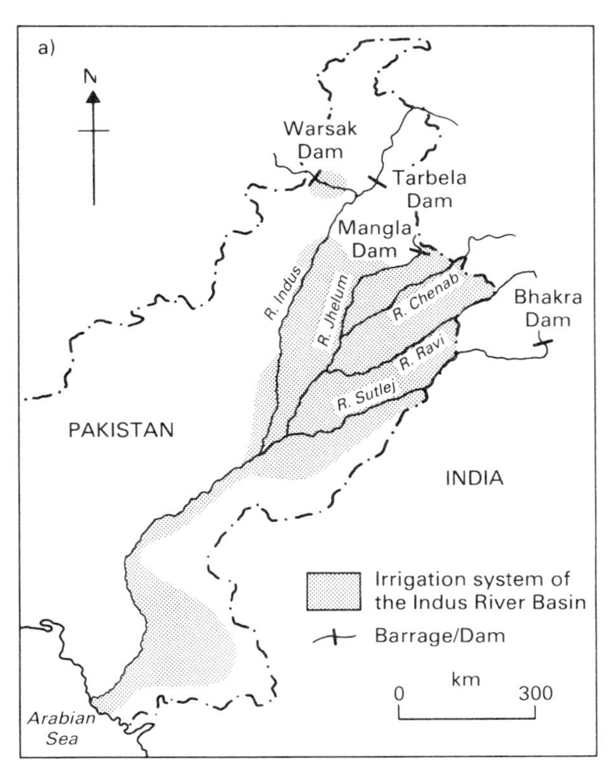

9.5a Irrigation systems on the Indo–Pakistan border

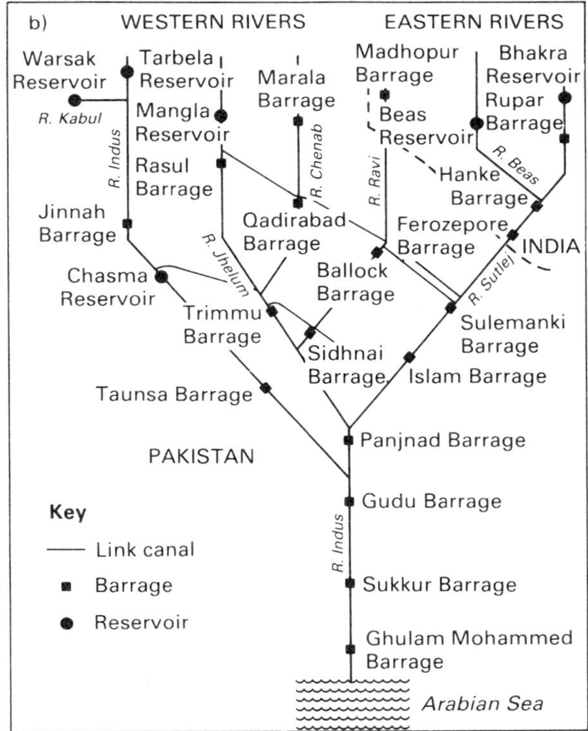

9.5b The Indus Waters Treaty; canal schemes for the Punjab

The main irrigated crop on the Indus plains is wheat, but barley, millet, cotton, maize, and sugar-cane are also grown taking advantage of the water supply. Production of rice has also increased, although in Pakistan it is grown principally for export rather than as a subsistence crop as in India. It is particularly popular in areas which have been subject to soil salinisation because some varieties are able to tolerate mildly saline conditions. The climate allows double or triple cropping in some carefully managed areas and crops are generally of high quality and have contributed towards Indian and Pakistani food supply and industrial growth but this has only been achieved by the use of the modern irrigation systems which have, in turn, wrought havoc on the natural drainage system of the Indus plains.

Before irrigation was introduced, the runoff from the monsoon rains found its way into natural drainage channels and eventually entered the river systems. The irrigation canals have intercepted the natural channels so a network of surface drains had to be constructed to take the runoff. Despite this, these have proved inadequate and with continued soak-in of water, the water-table has risen. In some areas where the water-table had previously been 27 m below the surface, it is now at, or approaching, surface level. As a result, waterlogging and soil salinisation have become major problems.

By the late 1950s some 24 300 ha of fertile cropland were going out of production each year. The attempted solutions, adopted by Pakistan's Water and Power Development Authority (WAPDA) are their Salinity Control and Reclamation Projects (SCARP) which aim to lower the ground-water table by making increased ground-water available for irrigation. By the late 1970s, WAPDA had installed over 11 000 tubewells throughout the Indus plains and a further 146 000 smaller-scale wells had been developed by private contractors. Although the water-table is falling again there have been several unanticipated problems. Salinity levels in the fresh-water tubewells are reported to be high and as a result the quality of irrigation water is impaired. This saline water pumped out of the tubewells, finds its way into the Indus channel leading to poorer water quality in the lower reaches of the Indus which could result in declining agricultural yields in that area.

6. What features of the monsoon climate have made it necessary to alter the natural hydrological cycle, and what form do these alterations usually take?

7. Why was it necessary for Pakistan to construct canals to link the Eastern and Western Rivers?

8. Describe and explain the ways in which the use of modern irrigation systems has 'wrought havoc on the natural drainage systems of the Indus plains' and outline the consequences for agricultural productivity.

9. What attempts are being made to solve these water resource problems and with what success?

India. Irrigation and the Green Revolution: case study

Pakistan has made considerable advances in the last 20 years in achieving a hydrological balance given the problems of the monsoon climate but only at the price of considerable capital investment in large-scale irrigation schemes. In India where similar schemes have been undertaken, at present less than 15% of farmland has access to irrigation, a total of 4 million ha. Although the irrigated area continues to increase, there are signs of a change in government attitudes towards investment in further large-scale irrigation projects. In the past, given the climatic problems, with most rainfall restricted to the four month monsoon, storage of water for irrigation has seemed the obvious way forward in increasing agricultural output and feeding the country's growing population. The introduction during the 1960s and 1970s of HYV of wheat and rice led to the Green Revolution and resulted in a one-third increase in cereal production (Fig. 9.6). This increase was achieved despite severe droughts in 1979 and 1980 indicating that water supply may have been of lesser importance than greater use

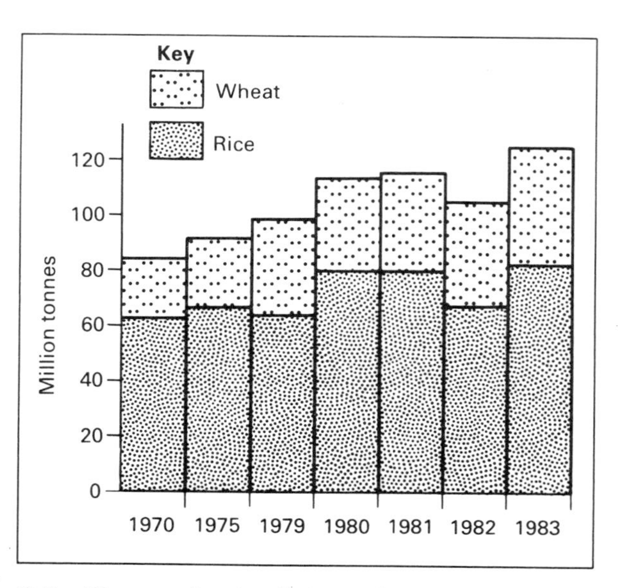

9.6 Rice production in India (1970–1983)

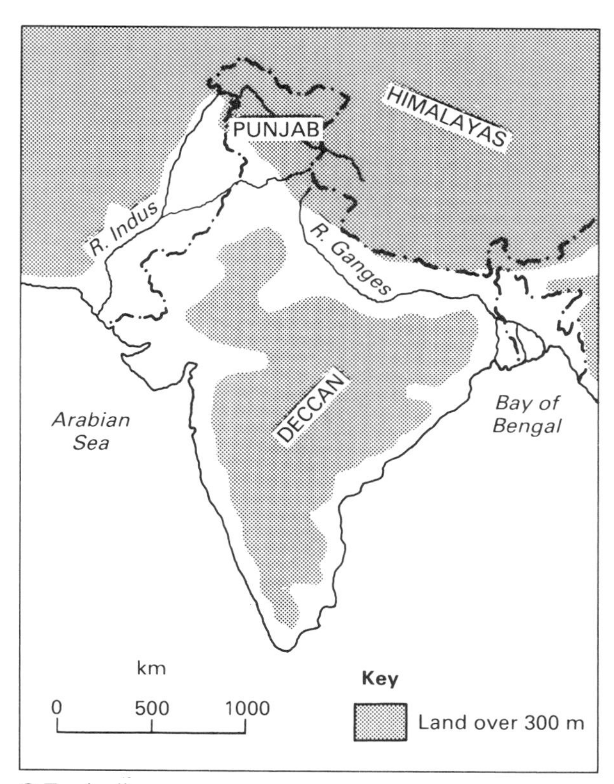

9.7 India

of fertilizers, pesticides and the new crop strains themselves. This has been borne out by a study of rice yields in India (1.8 tonnes per ha) and Japan (6 tonnes per ha) which concluded that the key difference was not water availability, but application of fertilizer. In Japan, the price of fertilizers was found to be 'vastly lower' in relation to what the farmers got for their rice. Hence Japanese rice farmers used 100 times more than their Indian counterparts. The study concluded:
'India . . . already has three times as much land under irrigation as had Japan — measured on a per capita basis. Yet India has invested large sums in recent years in still more irrigation. Had India invested enough of these sums to develop a low-cost efficient fertilizer industry, the payoff undoubtedly would have been much higher in terms of profitable increases in agricultural production.''

There are signs in the Punjab area of northern India (Fig. 9.7) that progress in agricultural development can be achieved where integrated planning has brought together a combination of improved farming methods, water control and land reform to consolidate small farms (55% of Indian farms are under 1 ha in size). Cereal yields in the Punjab now exceed those of Canada and the USA and the state is able to produce a considerable surplus towards feeding India's urban population. Unfortunately, this achievement has not spread to other parts of the country and it can also be argued that the main beneficiaries have been those farmers who had large consolidated landholdings and were already sufficiently affluent to be able to invest in fertilizers, pesticides and irrigation systems. Most of India's rural population still have little to show for the Green Revolution.

10. Why has there been a change in government attitudes towards further investment in large-scale irrigation projects in India?

11. What evidence is there of improved agricultural output in certain parts of India? Why is it likely that only a very small percentage of Indian farmers have gained any real benefit from the Green Revolution?

India. Deforestation and flooding in the Ganges basin: case study

The basin of the River Ganges (Fig. 9.7) occupies an area of almost 1 million km^2 — almost 25% of India's land area as well as extending some way into Bangladesh and Nepal. It is home to a population of over 200 million people and is the agricultural heartland of Northern India. To the north lie the Himalayas, the world's youngest and highest fold mountains and the source of the headwaters of two of the world's greatest rivers: the Indus flowing south-west into the Arabian Sea, and the Ganges, flowing towards the Bay of Bengal in the south-east. The entire Indo-Gangetic basin is perhaps best seen as a single environmental system. A system is a 'structural set of interactions' meaning that any changes in one part of a system will automatically produce changes in the others. Trees cut down in the Himalayas create bare slopes which yield more water and more sediment more quickly than slopes which retain their tree cover (Fig. 9.8). The effects of deforestation in Kashmir and increasing siltation in dams on the Indus and its tributaries has already been mentioned but the problem is now reaching such proportions that a recent report by India's Centre for Science and Environment revealed that:
'No other area of India's environment has been more viciously attacked and destroyed than the country's forests . . . the role of depletion of forests in the Himalayan ranges, which represent a quarter of India's forest reserves, is so great that this mighty mountain chain could become barren by the first half of the next century. From Kashmir

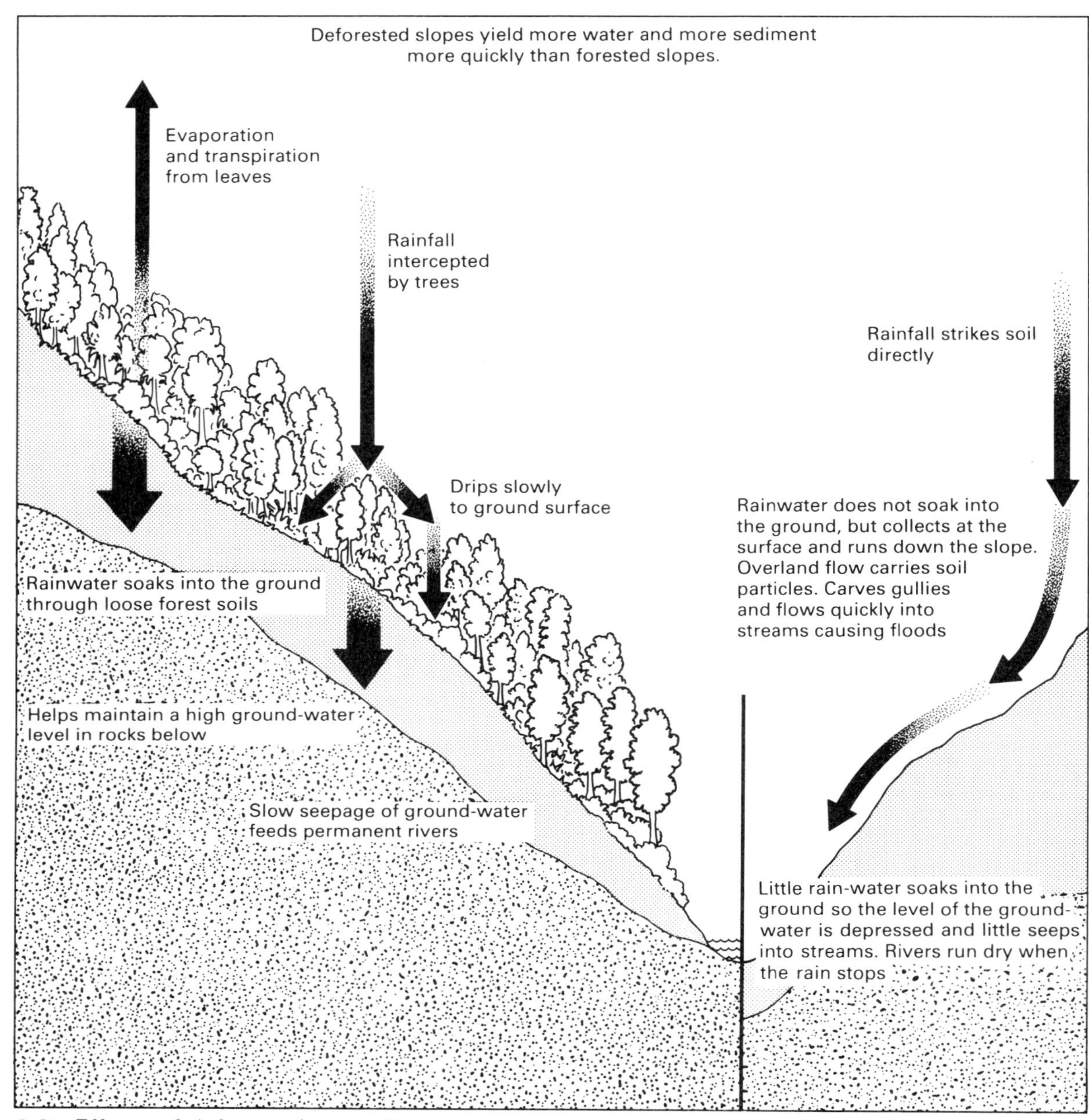

9.8 Effects of deforestation on slopes

to Assam the story is the same. Below 2000 metres there are literally no forests left. In the middle Himalayan belt which rises to an average height of 3000 metres, the forest area, originally a third of the total, has been reduced to about 8 per cent.'

The causes: Rising population pressures in India are usually illustrated by reference to the urban areas and the development of **bustees** but increases in rural areas can often create as many problems. In the Darjeeling district of West Bengal the 1872 census recorded a population of 95 000 living in an area which was almost entirely forested, by 1971 the population had increased to 8 million and the forested area had declined to about one-third. In the hill areas of northern India wood is the main source of fuel, it is used for cooking and for heating during the chilly nights and winters. It is cheaper than alternatives and estimates suggest that each person uses 0.5 tonnes of firewood every year. Nevertheless, it should not be assumed that deforestation is entirely attributable to the demands of the local population. During the second half of the 19th century the British began commercial timber exploitation and by the outbreak of the Great War many parts of the foothills had been heavily logged — with no reafforestation programmes. Destruction has continued as forests are damaged as trees are tapped for resin, logged for plywood and cut down to make way for settlements and farms in areas where malaria has been eradicated.

The effects: Soil erosion has now replaced tigers as the main menace in the foothills. It is estimated that deforestation-caused erosion results in an annual loss of 6 billion tonnes of soil. Apart from the consequences for the hill areas of this loss of valuable topsoil, the flooding and siltation caused by the soil downstream illustrate the connections within the system between the actions of the forty million people living in the mountain zone, on the 500 million who live in the Indo-Gangetic Plain. As a result of deforestation, the monsoon rains result in floods, followed by drought. In the 1978 monsoon season, 65 000 villages were flooded, 2000 people and more than 40 000 cattle drowned and extensive areas of fertile croplands ruined. The Indian government estimated total damage to property at more than US $2 billion. The Ganges now carries an average sediment load amounting to 1544 tonnes per km^2 of drainage basin (14 times higher than that of the Mississippi, which has a catchment area double the size). This is leading to a build up of silt on the river bed which in some areas is rising by one-sixth of a metre each year, causing worse flooding. Some parts of the river are being made unnavigable by mud shoals, and near the mouth, the ports of Calcutta and Dhaka are silting up. Further out in the Bay of Bengal a new island estimated at 50 000 km^2 is about to break the surface, caused by the accumulation of river sediment.

The solutions: Initially, the response of the Indian government was to increase spending on flood protection schemes along the Ganges — thereby dealing with the consequences of the problem, but not addressing the causes in the mountains. More recently, the Indian Army has been recruited to carry out large-scale tree-planting in the Himalayan foothills and the World Bank is making a loan of over US $40 million to promote reafforestation. A new government agency The Institute on Himalayan Environment and Development has been established to monitor land management in the Indian Himalayas. Perhaps one of the most encouraging developments in India has been the emergence of local groups such as the Chipko (Hug-the-Trees) movement, which aims to prevent further unnecessary destruction of woodland and foster good forestry practice. Eventually however it is likely that success can only be achieved with international co-operation, especially with Nepal where current rates of deforestation run at a terrifying 400 000 ha per year and the population is expected to increase from 16 million today to 23 million by the end of the century.

12. Explain why deforestation in the Himalayas can have disastrous effects in the Ganges Basin, hundreds of kilometres downstream.

13. Draw up a table and identify and explain the causes, effects and attempted solutions of the destruction of forest in the Himalayas. Explain why international co-operation will be a vital element in any final resolution of the problem.

10

Water resources II — the indirect use of water

Introduction

This chapter looks at the indirect use of water resources, where people do not actually make use of the water itself but rather of the resources which are to be found within either salt or fresh water. The latter part of the chapter goes on to deal with human misuse of our oceans, seas, lakes and rivers through a series of pollution case studies.

Inevitably most people tend to have a very land-centred view of the resources provided on the surface of the Earth but the 71% of its surface which is water constitutes a vast 'resource reservoir' which at present is arguably grossly under-used. Unfortunately not all of the resources provided by the oceans and seas are equally accessible as they exist within a reservoir of great depth and sub-sea landscape. Mount Everest (8848 m), for example, could easily be lost within the Mariana Trench in the western Pacific which sinks to 11 034 m at its southern end in the Challenger Deep (Fig. 10.1). These trenches,

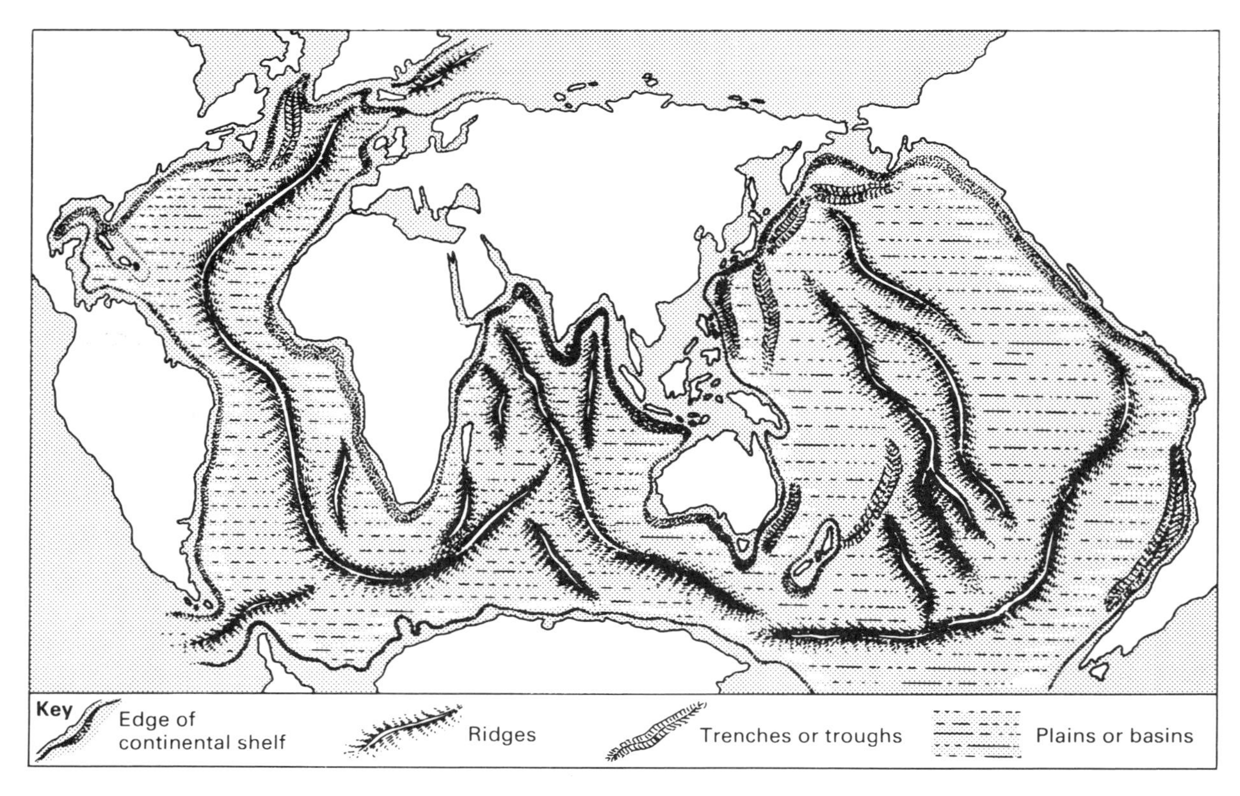

10.1 Sea-bed topography

which often run parallel and adjacent to the edges of the oceans, are complemented by mid-oceanic ridges which are sometimes 'capped' by islands which protrude above the surface. In contrast to these spectacular areas of ocean floor relief there are others which resemble the great plains found within the interior of our continental land-masses. The fringes of the oceans are marked by fertile **continental shelves** which cover approximately 8% of the total area of the oceans and form an environment rich in plant and fish life, and by the slopes which eventually lead down to the ocean depths.

Resources provided by the oceans and seas

At the outset it is useful to remember that scientists suspect that the oceans are where life on this planet actually first began. They believe that the first and simplest single-cell forms of life evolved as a result of the interaction between energy from the sun and nutrients in the water, a process which continues to this day. These very simple microflora or **phytoplankton** rely upon sunlight to generate growth and therefore tend to proliferate near to the surface.

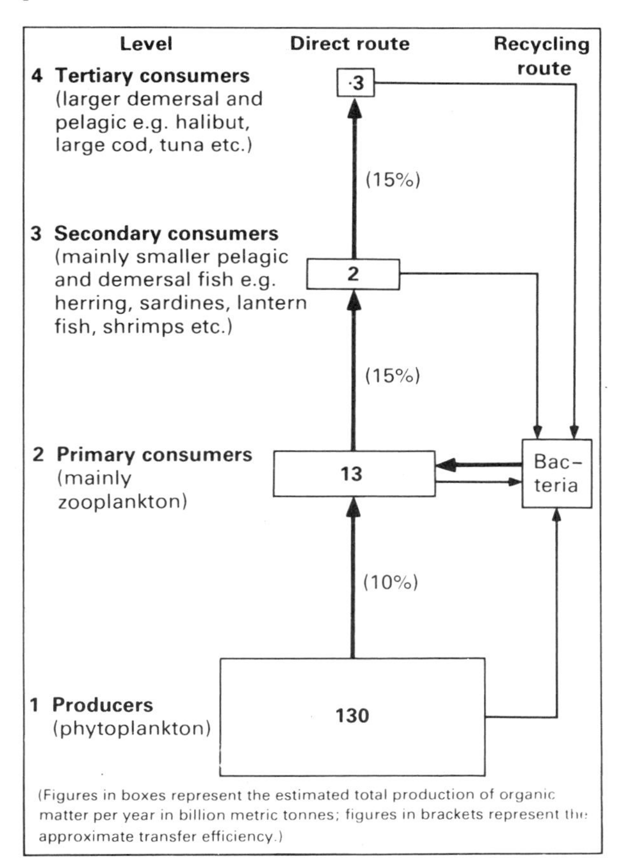

10.2 Simplified aquatic food chain

Phytoplankton (tiny 'drifting plants') form the first link in a food chain (Fig. 10.2) which then progresses through a primary consumer level largely of **zooplankton** (small sea-creatures) to the levels at which humans began to develop a resource interest, the secondary and tertiary consumer stages. The secondary consumers include the smaller **pelagic** (surface-dwelling) and **demersal** (floor-dwelling) varieties of fish while the tertiary consumers consist of the larger types of each (Fig. 10.2).

Fishing in inshore waters has gone on since the earliest times utilising a resource which provided and still provides a valuable source of protein for human beings. Between 1950 and the early 1970s the world catch of fish increased at a rate of 6–7% per year, reaching 73.5 million tonnes by 1976. Since then the catch has fluctuated somewhat, largely due to problems associated with over-fishing. These difficulties have been particularly acute off the shores of certain developed countries where the competing demands of nations with highly sophisticated and technologically advanced fishing fleets have led to depletion of stocks and catch quotas being imposed. The North Sea herring fishery is just one case in point. Fishing for anchoveta off the coast of Peru in the 1970s is perhaps the most celebrated example of over-exploitation and gross depletion in the developing world. More recently the biggest single-species fishery in the world has been for Alaska pollack, which in 1975–76 peaked at 5 million tonnes but has slumped ever since to less than 4 million tonnes.

According to certain fishery experts the potential annual catch from the world's oceans could be increased to over 100 million tonnes using existing technology, if consumers could be re-educated to accept certain types of fish at present regarded for various reasons as being 'unpalatable'. Currently the great bulk of the fish consumed comes from the pelagic and demersal groups, whereas **crustaceans**, e.g. shellfish, lobsters and shrimps and **cephalopods**, e.g. squid and octopus are relatively poorly represented. Further expansion of the existing fish catch could result from the development of fisheries harvesting Bering Sea flatfish, Atlantic grenadier and Pacific sandlance and sauries, for example. The northern hemisphere, where several fisheries are already fished to the limit, at present takes approximately 60% of the total world fish catch but appears to have the potential to produce at least 40% more (see Fig. 10.3).

In the southern hemisphere on the other hand the proportions are reversed with 40% of the total catch being caught there and the potential

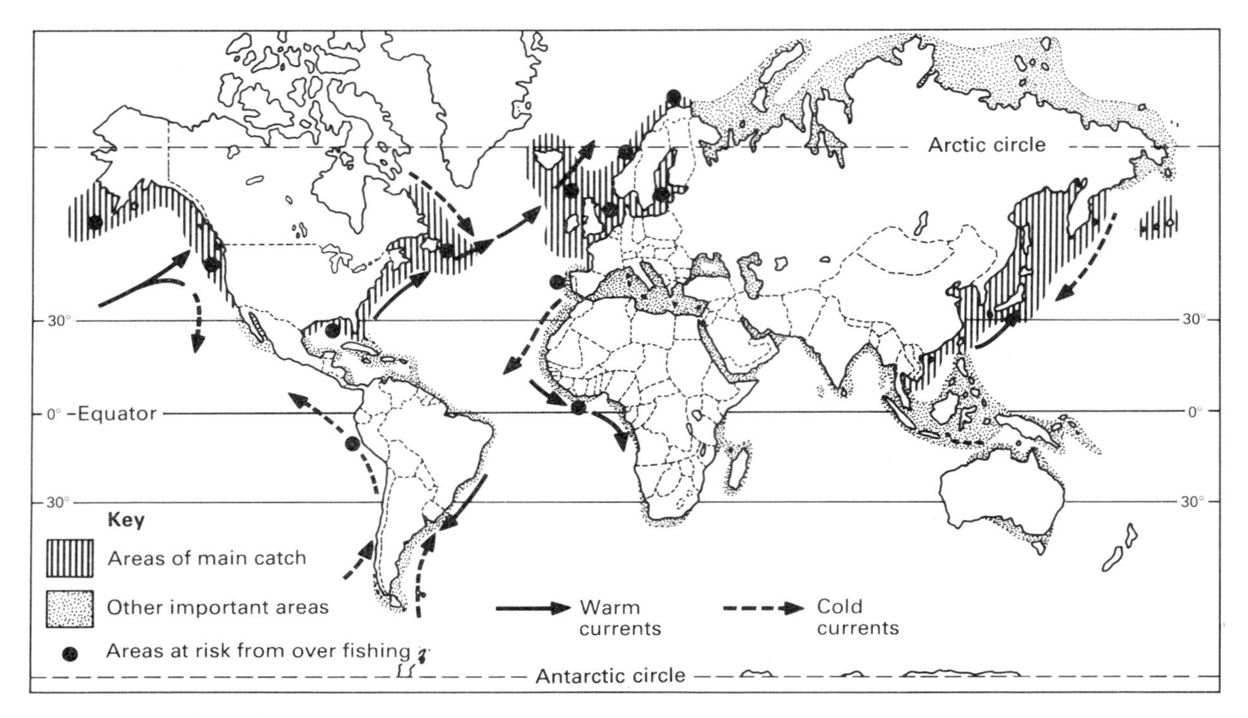

10.3 World fisheries

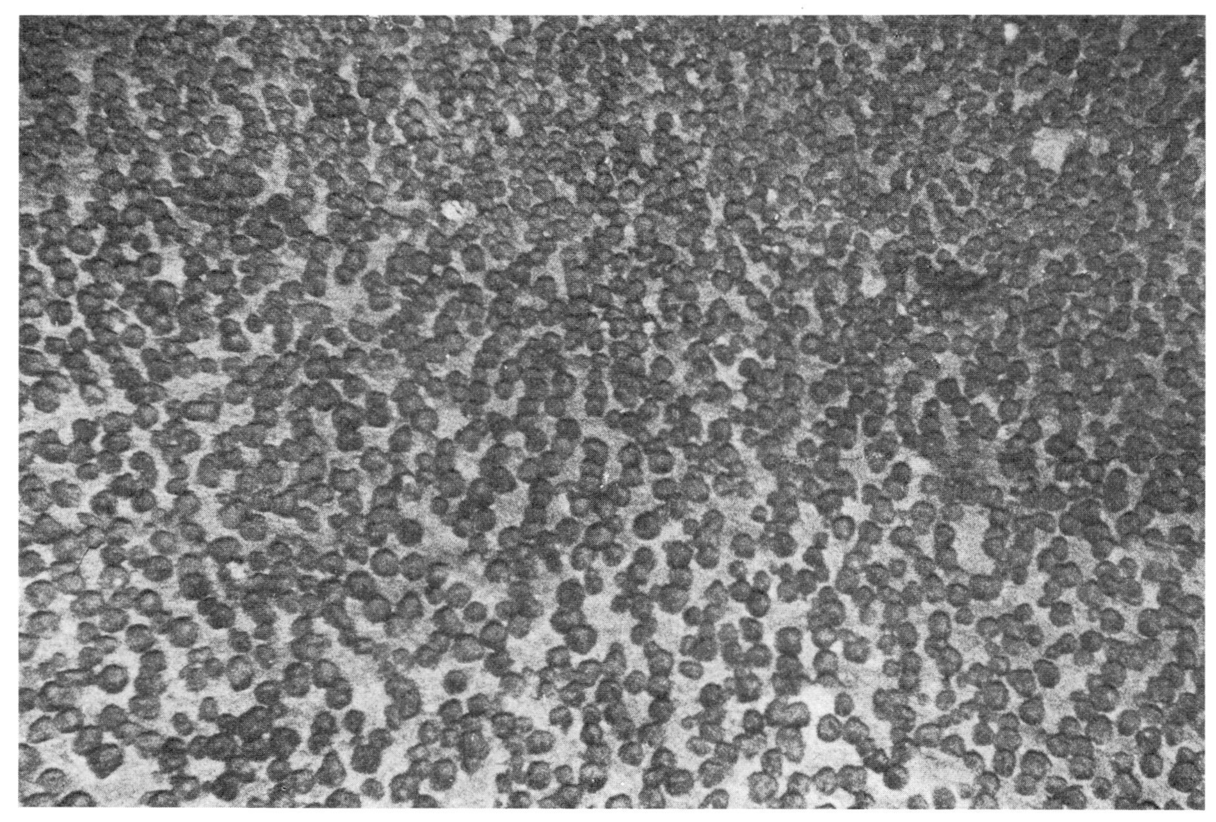

10.4 Manganese nodules dredged from the sea bed. Average diameter of each nodule 5cm

existing to increase this total to at least 60% more. The Southern Ocean also contains vast reserves of a tiny shrimp-like creature called krill, of which only 2% of the potential 50 million tonne catch per year is currently harvested largely by Poland, Japan and the USSR. Two further possible ways of expanding world fish catch could be through fish farming and further exploiting fresh water sources in lakes and rivers.

Perhaps the most infamous example of the overexploitation of marine creatures is the example of the whale. In the past the oil, meat, blubber and the skin of these animals was so prized that the larger baleen (plankton-consuming) whales such as the blue, humpback and fin, in addition to certain of the predatory sperm whales, were hunted to virtually commercial extinction. Although the imposition of strict quotas by the International Whaling Commission has allowed some recovery of stocks, certain non-member states continued to exploit these endangered species until the early 1980s whilst some member states have switched their attention to smaller types such as the minke and sei. Other types of sea creatures, such as dolphins, porpoises and even seals have also been subject to sporadic threats of over-use in different areas of the world in the past.

Manganese	25–35%
Nickel	1– 2%
Copper	1– 2%
Cobalt	0.1– 0.5%
Molybdenum	0.001– 0.01%
Vanadium	0.001– 0.01%
Other metals e.g. iron, zinc, lead	smaller quantities

10.5 Typical mineral content of manganese nodules

In contrast to sea mammals such as the whale the mineral resources contained within and beneath the oceans are relatively under-exploited. Certain of these are actually dissolved within the water itself, salt in particular having been extracted by evaporation in the past. More recently bromine and magnesium have also been extracted by various chemical processes and Japan, with a fast-developing nuclear power industry, hopes to remove uranium in future.

The continental shelves remain a valuable source of minerals. Large-scale dredging for sands, gravels and even shells (for cement) occurs off countries such as Japan, USA and Britain.

Even more valuable resources increasingly being exploited beneath the continental shelves are oil and natural gas deposits. Off-shore drilling was pioneered in the USA towards the end of the last century but the rising cost of oil, especially since the early 1970s, has allowed the development of platforms and drilling equipment capable of use towards the edge of the continental shelves at greater and greater depths. In the near future we may also see the beginnings of a mining operation at very great depths indeed, perhaps even below 4000 m. These operations will seek to recover potato-sized, crumbly and irregular shaped 'manganese nodules' (Fig. 10.4) from the deep-sea 'plains' on the ocean floor, e.g. to the south east of Hawaii in the Pacific. Despite being called 'manganese nodules' these accretions also contain other valuable minerals and could be mined using existing vacuum-pumping techniques of dredging the sea floor if commercially viable.

The world's constantly increasing demands for energy have led to greater and greater interest in oceans, seas and estuaries for the purposes of 'tapping' the potential of tides, waves and even the great differences in temperature between water at the surface and at the bottom. Several examples already exist of power stations which utilise wave and tide power, e.g. at Le Rance in France and at Toftöy in Norway, and others, e.g. the Solway and Severn estuaries in Britain, have had detailed plans seriously proposed. Further indirect uses of water include recreation, and perhaps the most prominent use of all in the past, for the purposes of sea transport and trade.

1. 'In many ways the floors of the oceans offer more varied and spectacular relief than is to be found on land.' Explain this statement with reference to Fig. 10.1.

2. Where within the oceans is the greatest proliferation of plant and fish life to be found? Suggest why this should be the case.

3. Study Fig. 10.2. Account for the fact that even the largest sea-creatures rely upon phytoplankton, the simplest of sea-life, in order to survive.

4. With reference to at least one example of overfishing from the developed world assess the reasons for overfishing and outline strategies introduced to prevent repetition.

5. Why has it been said that the oceans 'could provide a much larger proportion of world food supply if required to do so in the future'? Quote actual examples to support your answer.

6. Apart from fishing, in what other ways could the resources of the oceans be exploited by humans?

The misuse of rivers, lakes, seas and oceans

Through the passage of time the world's rivers have acted as a vast transportation network carrying huge quantities of eroded materials and depositing them into the giant purification system of our seas and oceans. Increasingly, however, our rivers, lakes, seas and oceans have been asked to accept more and more of the waste end-products of all sorts of human resource processes. Inevitably the accumulation of human-generated sewage sludge, industrial effluents, fertilizer and pesticide residues, and even radioactive waste has resulted in severe pollution problems in certain rivers, lakes, seas and oceans at various points in time. The case studies which follow seek to highlight examples of pollution which have reached or are near crisis point and the strategies adopted to cope.

The River Rhine: case study

Problems of pollution in rivers which run across or along international frontiers are always particularly difficult to solve because they inevitably involve a concerted and co-ordinated plan of action requiring the co-operation of all the nations which have land lying within its basin. The Rhine is a classic example flowing as it does through four countries and passing along its course several major conurbations and the industrial heartland of Western Europe (see Fig. 10.6).

The Rhine rises in the Alps in Switzerland and remains relatively unpolluted until the final part of its course within that country where in and around the city of Basle a vast complex of chemical and pharmaceutical factories has grown up. On the western side of the Rhine Rift Valley the French province of Alsace has for a long time been the home of an extensive potash mining operation, part of the residue of which has contributed to the salination of the River Rhine. In West Germany the River Rhine and its tributaries drain a river basin which includes the industrial heartland of that country, the Rhine-Ruhr conurbation, and several other major conurbations e.g. around Bonn, Cologne, Frankfurt and Stuttgart. Vast amounts of often only partially

Key
C Major chemical plants
S Major steel plants
o Other major industries
● Cities
—· International frontiers
Section of river which suffered most severe pollution and ecological damage

Site of accident at Sandoz chemical plant, 1 November 1986

10.6 The course of the River Rhine

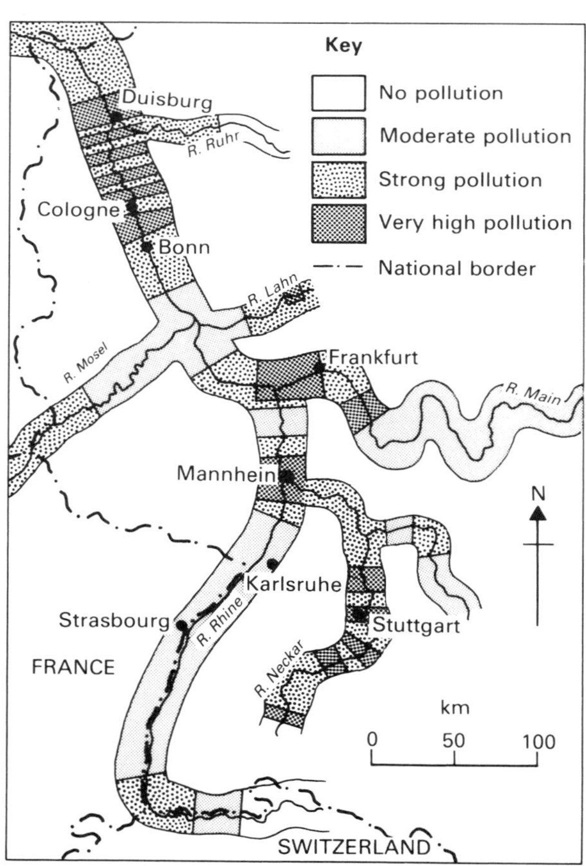

10.7 Pollution levels along the middle course of the Rhine

treated human and industrial waste are still discharged into the Rhine river system within Germany but improvements have steadily taken place (see Fig. 10.7 for pollution levels in 1967). By the time the waters of the Rhine reach the Netherlands they are not just contaminated by human and industrial waste, they have also been raised in temperature through repeated use for cooling purposes and are affected by runoff containing traces of herbicides and pesticides from agricultural land. Unfortunately the Dutch are forced to rely upon the Rhine for a significant proportion of their water supply. The Rhine Delta scheme (Fig. 5.5), which was due for completion in 1985, includes the provision of several fresh-water lakes formed through the damming of certain distributaries of the Rhine. Water from these sources will require extensive purification prior to domestic or agricultural (irrigation) use.

During the 1950s and 1960s pressure gradually mounted to clean up what had become known as 'the sewer of Europe'. In 1963 the International Commission For The Protection Of The Rhine was set up but relatively little success was actually achieved until 1976 when the Bonn accord on cleaning up the Rhine was signed by the affected nations. One of the first problems tackled under the accord was supposed to be the reduction of salt discharge from the Alsatian potash mines but the French took 3 years to resolve technical difficulties over underground storage of the waste and 7 years to fully ratify the treaty. Later agreements have limited the disposal of certain types of chemical waste into the river such that by 1986 thirteen or fourteen species of fish could survive in the river (compared to only three or four, fifteen years previously) including sensitive varieties such as trout and salmon.

By 1986 considerable improvements had taken place in the river when on 1st November 1986 (and similar to previous occasions of much more limited scale and consequence), an accident occurred as a result of a fire at the Sandoz chemical plant near Basle causing some 30 tonnes of a lethal chemical cocktail of herbicides, fungicides and pesticides to be washed into the river.The immediate effects of the disaster were horrendous as almost all river life for a distance of 300 km downriver as far as Mainz was killed off. It has been estimated that well over half a million fish, including 150 000 eels, died and had to be scooped from the river. Further downstream the consequences for the human population could have been worse as German towns could switch their domestic supplies to ground-water sources and in the Netherlands the sluice gates in the dykes enclosing the Rhine were shut directing the toxic river waters straight out into the North Sea.

There appears to be no doubt that the middle course of the River Rhine (Fig. 10.7), including its tributaries which remained remarkably unaffected by the spillage, will recover and that river life will regenerate over a period of five to ten years. But how long will it take to get Switzerland, a non-member of the European Community and with notoriously lax controls over its chemical industry, to work together with France, Germany and the Netherlands to ensure that a further 'accident' never again occurs to set back the environmental regeneration of the river?

The Great Lakes: case study

Lakes Superior, Michigan, Huron, Erie and Ontario together form the world's largest freshwater system which is collectively known as the 'Great Lakes' of North America (see Fig. 10.8). In the past the Great Lakes were a naturally regulating system but the third quarter of this century saw greatly increased human interference which resulted in the need for strict controls on water extraction by both Canada and the USA.

Similar to the Rhine River basin in Europe, the Great Lakes basin of North America became a very important industrial area, encompassing several rapidly expanding cities during the first half of this century. Unfortunately the Great Lakes received the major proportion of the waste products from these highly industrialised urban areas until, in 1958, Dr Alfred Beeton in preparing a report on Lake Erie concluded that:

'The 10 000 square mile lake was dying, through a process of eutrophication. Vast influxes of pollutants, primarily nitrogen and phosphorus from sewage and fertilisers, were stimulating the growth of algae and dying algae were creating oxygen demands that suffocated fish.'

(Thomas Canby, *National Geographic*, August 1980)

The gradual process of enrichment known as **eutrophication** had earlier resulted in almost total change in fish species and plant-life within the lake and the build up of ugly piles of **cladophora algae**, especially in summer, on its surface. No concerted action to remedy the pollution problems of the Great Lakes actually took place until an incident on the Cuyahoga River in July 1969. This river, which flows into Lake Erie at Cleveland (Fig. 10.8), was inundated with debris and oil which actually caught fire, causing considerable damage to two railway bridges and property alongside the river. The incident served a very useful purpose however as it drew to the attention of both government and public the sorry state into which Lake Erie in particular, and certain of the rivers which feed it, had fallen.

Partly as a result of the Cuyahoga River fire the 1970s saw the beginnings of the 'ecological renaissance' of the Great Lakes as the US Congress enacted far-reaching water pollution legislation. By 1980 even the waters of Lake Erie were showing signs of significant recuperation and the Cuyahoga River at Cleveland had been sufficiently cleaned up to attract not just fish but also fishermen and others interested in water based recreation.

The Persian Gulf: case study

In the past the sea and ocean areas of the world have been seen as a dumping ground for the waste products of many human-engendered activities. By the early 1970s the need for controls was widely recognised and in 1973 the International Convention for the Prevention of Pollution from Ships (known as MARPOL) was formulated. This convention set out to strictly regulate all forms of pollution from ships and laid down minimum distances from the shore where waste could be discharged, e.g. treated garbage — 3 nautical miles; treated sewage — 4 nautical miles; untreated sewage, untreated garbage, some toxic wastes — 12 nautical miles; oil residues — 50 nautical miles. The convention also imposed an outright ban on disposal of toxic wastes in the Baltic and Black Seas and on the discharge of oil in the Baltic, Black, Mediterranean and Red Seas and the Persian Gulf. By 1983, twenty-five nations had ratified the MARPOL convention.

This international convention has been complemented by a series of 10 more localised initiatives

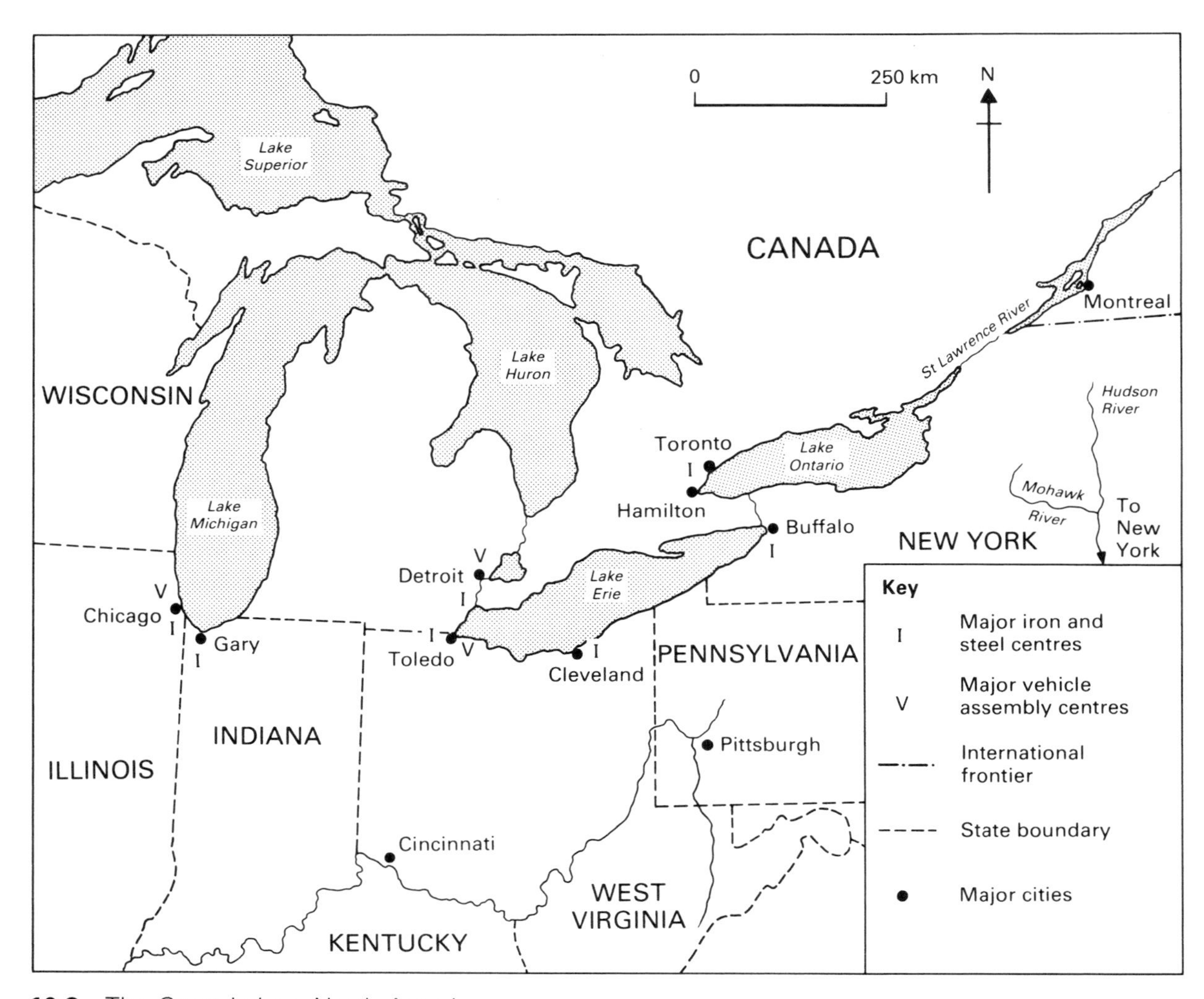

10.8 The Great Lakes, North America

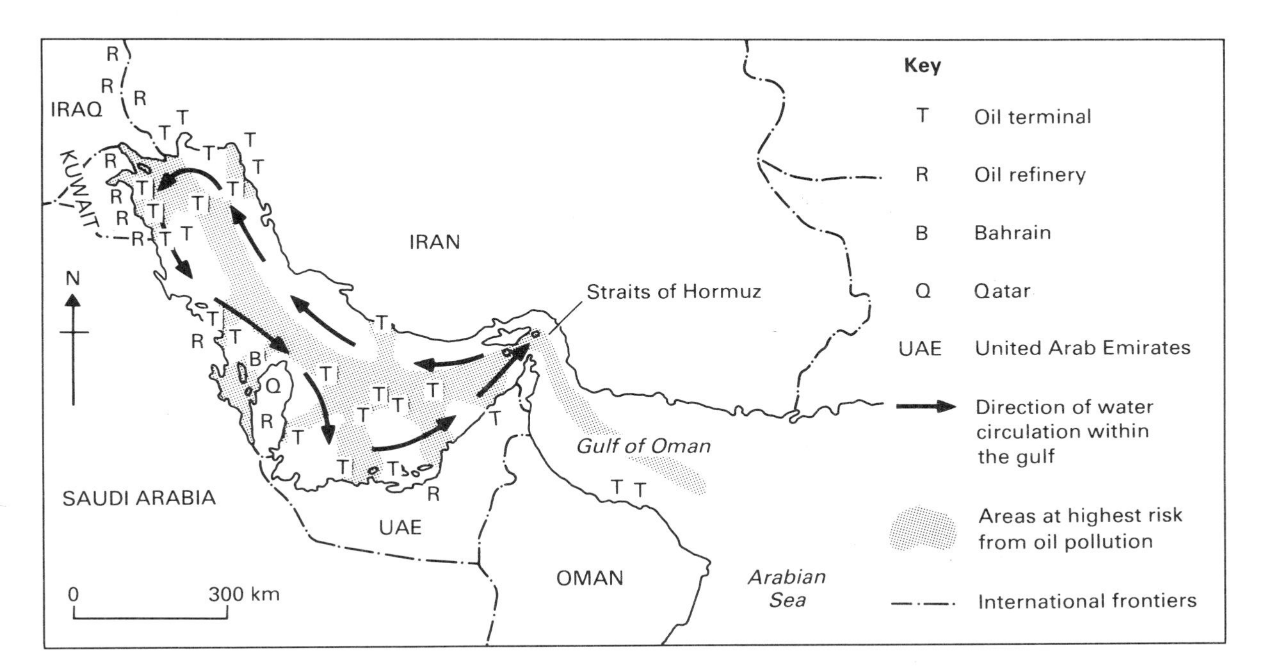

10.9 The Persian Gulf

under the UN Environment Programme's 'Regional Seas Programme'. These initiatives were launched to clean up coastal waters, especially in landlocked or semi-enclosed seas, and began in 1975 with the Mediterranean Action Plan closely followed in 1976 by the Kuwait Action Plan (covering the Persian Gulf) and roughly one per year ever since including the Red Sea and the Caribbean.

The Persian Gulf is a shallow and almost landlocked area of sea (Fig. 10.9) which receives very little fresh inflow of water and virtually no rainfall. It suffers very high levels of evaporation and is very salty and is only slowly replenished by the flow of water through the narrow Straits of Hormuz. This insignificant exchange of water with the Indian Ocean means that the Persian Gulf is a very fragile environment, particularly sensitive to even small amounts of pollution.

The eight oil-rich states which are grouped around the Persian Gulf are amongst the fastest developing nations in the world and have rapidly increasing populations. These increasing populations have placed basic services such as sewage and garbage disposal under increasing pressure especially in coastal areas where most people live. As a result most countries have large public works programmes underway but in the early 1980s Bahrain for example still deposited three-quarters of its untreated sewage into the Persian Gulf. The new industries being developed around the Gulf (see Fig. 10.9), are also required to have their patterns of waste disposal closely monitored under the Kuwait Action Plan.

By far the most dangerous pollution threat however is posed by the oil industry and its related activities. Accidental spillage at terminals (see Fig. 10.9) or during transfer; offshore blowouts; tankers washing out their tanks or deballasting; leakages from pipelines; and, during the Iran–Iraq war, tankers ruptured and immobilised by missile attack could have a cumulative and potentially devastating effect on the fragile gulf ecosystem. Strange though it may seem, the onset of the Iran–Iraq war helped to ensure that certain of the objectives of the Kuwait Action Plan have been more easily met due to giant supertankers lying at anchor outside the Straits of Hormuz in the Gulf of Oman while waiting for a berth at one of the many terminals in the Persian Gulf. These empty supertankers carry water (which is heavily contaminated with oil) as ballast which they then dump into the sea prior to picking up their cargo. In the past, oil tankers serving Saudi terminals alone are thought to have discharged as much as half a million tonnes of oil but now the problem with that pollution has been transferred outside of the Persian Gulf to the Gulf of Oman, resulting in widespread contamination of the beaches of Oman itself.

The transfer of the tanker deballasting problem from one area of sea to another is a further indication that short-term success in protecting one area may lead to an increased threat to another. At the end of the day the world must be made to realise that pollution must be controlled at its source and then begin to clear up the legacy it has left from the past.

Managing the oceans

Several of the issues referred to earlier in this chapter e.g. the over-exploiting of many fisheries, the near extermination of certain types of whale and the various examples of the effects of pollution have shown how we are placing the abundant resources found in our waters in increasing jeopardy. As this century has progressed, so the need for international agreements to control human use of the seas and oceans in particular has become more and more pressing. A series of United Nations Conferences on the Law of the Sea (UNCLOS) have now been held in an attempt to secure agreement on resource allocation and management for the seas and oceans.

The third UNCLOS, which eventually ended on 30 April 1982 after 9 years of intermittent discussion, did produce a treaty which placed 40% of the total ocean area under the direct jurisdiction of coastal nations (Fig. 10.10), leaving the traditional 'freedom of the seas' over the remaining 60%. Although 134 nations did sign the treaty initially, relatively few have actually gone ahead and ratified it, actually accepting its provisions as law. In addition certain of the leading maritime nations, such as the USA, UK and West Germany, did not sign largely because of the clauses relating to mineral deposits on the ocean floor. Unfortunately it now appears unlikely that the necessary sixty states will ratify the treaty thus preventing it from becoming part and parcel of international law.

In many ways the failure of nations to ratify the law of the sea convention and to recognise the resources of the deep sea-bed as the 'common heritage of mankind' paints a dismal picture of our ability to manage our planet's resources. It is, however, an indication of the willingness of nations to sit down and discuss resource issues which may have been the subject of more violent conflict in the past. If this spirit of co-operation can continue to be fostered and we learn from earlier mistakes then the Earth's land and water resources may be much better managed in future.

7. Using a simple annotated flow diagram list the human uses of our rivers, lakes, seas and oceans at the following 'points' in time:
   prehistoric times; Middle Ages; present day; future?

8. Explain why the 20th century has brought increasing problems of river pollution in both the developed and less developed worlds.

9. a) Referring to more than one of the pollution case studies, describe the difficulties associated with any concerted plan of action.
   b) Despite these difficulties, outline how progress has been made in each of your examples.

10. a) Using actual examples, assess whether human efforts at managing the oceans have been successful or otherwise.
    b) In your opinion, does this bode well or ill for efforts to better manage land and water resources in future? Give reasons for your answer.

Title	Extent (nautical miles from land)	Provisions
1. Territorial sea	12	Sovereign rights guaranteed
2. Contiguous zone	24	Control for limited purposes
3. Exclusive economic zone	200	Functional rights over economic activity, scientific research and environmental preservation
4. Continental shelf	varies	Right to explore and exploit

10.10 UNCLOS zones under national jurisdiction

Glossary

Acidification the development of soil acidity

Acid rain rain contaminated by chemicals (notably sulphur dioxide, producing dilute sulphuric acid) which have been released from industrial chimneys

Aquifers layers of rock which hold water and allow water to percolate through them

Azonal soils soils which have not been sufficiently subject to soil-forming processes for the development of a mature profile and so are little changed from the parent rock material

Basin irrigation flood waters of a river are led onto the basin-shaped plots of land, each of which is surrounded by embankments

Bio-climatic zones or biomes an organic community of plants and animals, viewed within its physical environment or habitat

Biosphere a term sometimes applied to that portion of the Earth occupied by the various forms of life

Biotic pertaining to plant life

Boreal forests the largely coniferous forests occupying vast areas of North America and Eurasia mainly between the latitudes 45°N and 75°N

Bustees shanty towns found in and around cities in India

Cephalopods large marine molluscs e.g. cuttle-fish, octopus

Chinook the warm, dry, seasonal wind experienced along the eastern side of the Rocky Mountains in Canada and the USA

Cladophora algae plants which can flourish on the surface of water which is heavily polluted

Cloud seeding the dropping from aircraft of particles of dry ice, silver iodine or other substances into clouds, in an attempt to stimulate precipitation

Conduction air being heated through contact with the earth's surface

Continentality a climatic effect resulting in extremes of temperature within the interior of large land masses

Continental shelves the submerged, gently sloping margins of a continent

Convection a term describing vertical movements of air within the atmosphere

Convectional rainfall precipitation arising from currents of warm air rising into the atmosphere and condensing to form clouds

Crustaceans crabs, lobsters, shrimps — anthropod animals

Cyclonic rainfall rain associated with the passage of a cyclone or depression, and caused by a warm, moist air mass moving upwards over colder, heavier air

Czernozems very fertile soil of subhumid steppe, consisting of a dark topsoil over a lighter calcareous layer. In Russia — black earth.

Deforestation the complete felling and clearance of forested land

Demersal fish which feed near the sea floor

Desertification the spread of desert conditions into former areas of semi-arid bush, steppe grassland and even woodland, principally caused by human activity

Desertization desert advancement principally as a result of climatic factors

Dew point the temperature at which the atmosphere, being cooled, becomes saturated with water vapour, and by condensation the latter is deposited as drops of dew

Diurnal range the amount of variation between the maximum and minimum of any element, such as air temperature, during 24 hours

Epiphytic plants which grow upon other plants i.e. they use the host plant for support, not nutrition

Eutrophication the gradual depletion of oxygen in marine environments as a result of pollution

Extensification development and expansion — usually applied to agriculture

Front the line of separation at the earth's surface between cold and warm air masses

Gleying	gley soil — a soil developed under conditions of intermittent waterlogging. The soils are sticky, compact and display no recognizable soil structure
Greenhouse effect	the earth's atmosphere permits the passage of short-wave solar energy to the earth's surface but greatly absorbs the long wave radiation from the earth, particularly when there's substantial cloud cover. Temperatures at the earth's surface are thus maintained at a higher level — the atmosphere acting like the glass of a greenhouse
Gullies	large channels
Hardpan	a compacted layer which can impede drainage through soil
Heat budget	balance between the heat gained by and lost from the Earth's atmosphere
Horizons	layers of soil which lie more or less parallel to the surface and have fairly distinctive soil properties
Humus	decomposed organic matter in the soil
Hydrosphere	all the water of the earth e.g. oceans, seas, lakes, ice-sheets etc and also the water that is present in the atmosphere
Insolation	the heat energy from the sun which reaches the earth in the form of short wave ultra-violet rays, visible light and infra-red rays
Intrazonal soil	a soil which has been influenced in its development less by climate and vegetation than by other factors such as defective drainage, excessive evaporation, or on unusual parent material
Irrigation	the artificial distribution and application of water to the land to stimulate, or make possible, the growth of plants in an otherwise too arid climate
Isotherms	lines on a map joining places which have the same temperature, or have the same average temperature
Kharif	crops largely grown during the rainy season in monsoon lands
Laterite	a reddish rock material produced by weathering and occurring near the surface, chiefly in humid, tropical regions
Latifundios	large landed estates found in Spain and parts of Latin America
Latosol	a major soil type associated with the humid tropics, and characterised by red, reddish-brown or yellow colouring
Leaching	the process by which soluble substances such as organic and mineral salts are washed out of the upper layers of a soil into a lower layer by percolating rain water
Lithosphere	the solid crust which envelopes the inner Barysphere of the earth
Ozone	an atmospheric layer which filters harmful solar radiation
Pelagic	fish which swim and feed near the surface of water
Perennial irrigation	a system of supplying water to land all year round
Permafrost	ground which is permanently frozen
Photosynthesis	a process whereby plants take in carbon dioxide through the leaves to promote growth and lose water vapour to the atmosphere
Phytoplankton	microscopic organisms found within the sea
Podzols	bleached, sandy soils, poor in humus
Primary forest	when vegetation develops on a 'natural' site (that is, not created by people)
Rabi	crops grown mainly during the dry season in Monsoon lands
Reforestation	the planting of trees on land where a forest has previously stood, but has been destroyed
Relief or orographic rainfall	rain which is caused by moisture laden air being forced to rise over high land
Rendzina	a dark-coloured intrazonal soil which has developed under grass on limestone or chalk
Renewable resources	natural phenomenon which can be rejuvenated within a reasonably short time-scale
Resources	a feature of the environment used in order to meet particular human needs
Rills	small channels or gullies
Savanna	a type of African vegetation which is transitional between the rainforests of the humid tropics and the short grass and scrub of the hot desert margins

Secondary forest where people create new sites by the destruction of the existing vegetation (as in shifting cultivation)

Sedenterisation a Nigerian government programme to try and persuade nomadic tribesmen to take up settled jobs — even in towns

Selvas an alternative term for tropical rainforest, originally applied to the Amazon Basin but now used more generally

Silviculture cultivation of trees (forestry)

Subsoil the layer of material lying below the true soil or topsoil

Summer fallowed land left uncultivated during the summer months

Taiga the coniferous forest lands of the northern hemisphere

Transhumance the seasonal migration of people and animals to fresh pastures

Transpiration the process by which plants, having taken in moisture through their roots, return it to the atmosphere through their leaves in the form of water vapour

Water cycle the circulation of water from the oceans to the atmosphere, thence to the land and so back to the oceans

Xerophytic plants which have adapted to live in regions where little moisture is available e.g. cacti

Zero tillage land which has not been ploughed

Zones the five regions or belts into which the Earth is divided

Zooplankton floating and drifting animal life